How to Be a Responsible Mother:

A Workbook for Offenders

Diane E. Stawar, M.A.

Terry L. Stawar, Ed.D.

Mission of the American Correctional Association
The American Correctional Association provides a professional organization for all individuals and groups, both public and private, that share a common goal of improving the justice system.

Production and cover by Capitol Communication Systems, Inc.
Illustrations courtesy of Janie Paul, Prison Creative Arts Project, University of Michigan, Ann Arbor.
All of the illustrations by inmate artists are used with permission.

Printed in the United States of America by Gasch Printing, Odenton, MD.

For information on publications and videos available from ACA, go to our website: www.aca.org

ISBN: 978-56991-300-0

You may order this publication from:
American Correctional Association
206 N. Washington St., Suite 200
Alexandria, VA 22314
1-800-222-5646 ext. 0129

Table of Contents

Introduction for Inmates

Being a Mother

This workbook is about being a mom and learning how to become an even better one. Being a mother is one of the hardest jobs in the world. Being a mother is much more than just having children. Motherhood is a lifetime job. It requires a woman to look at herself and her responsibilities closely. Being a mother is something that no one can ever take away from you. It is your connection with the future. It may be your best chance to change the world in a positive way.

Mothers Who Are Offenders

In America, more than two million children have at least one parent in prison or jail, according to the Bureau of Justice Statistics. Children suffer many negative effects from having their mother in prison. Children may become confused, afraid, or feel guilt and shame. Children with a mother in prison are at risk for emotional problems. They have increased chances of being arrested and incarcerated themselves.

Offenders who learn to become better mothers can help reduce these risks. Offenders can have positive effects on their children's lives. There is no better way you can spend your time than learning to be a better mom. Research shows that inmates who learn to become better mothers have fewer problems during their incarceration. They are less likely to return to prison, and their children adjust better when they are reunited.

The Importance of Mothers

Current research shows that nothing is more important to a child than a mother's love. How children do in school, what type of job they get, and how successful they are in relationships are all related to the security that stems from having a responsible mother. Children with loving mothers are more likely to do well in school, have healthy self-esteem, and get along better with others. These children are also more likely to avoid drug abuse, truancy, and criminal activity.

How to Use this Workbook

This workbook is your property. It will help you learn the skills and attitudes needed to become a better mother. The workbook will explain many important aspects of effective motherhood. The workbook will ask you to answer questions to help you learn. At times, the workbook asks you to write your personal thoughts and feelings—like a diary or journal. It will take courage to face some of the difficult personal issues discussed in this workbook.

Benefits and Goals: Why You Should Bother

Here are the things you will accomplish through the careful study of this workbook:

- You will prepare to become a better mother by:
    - Developing attitudes that lead to success
    - Overcoming painful experiences from the past
    - Managing personal stress, fears, and frustration
    - Gaining knowledge about motherhood
    - Learning practical child-management skills.
- You will be able to identify and describe the effects your behavior and incarceration has on your children and family.
- You will be able to identify and learn useful skills for dealing with loss, shame, and guilt.
- You will be able to describe what children are like as they grow older.
- You will be able to choose the best discipline method for children at different ages.
- You will learn effective ways to communicate with your children's father(s) and other family members.
- You will make your own parenting and reunification plan.

If you do not have children now, but plan to have a family someday, this workbook can prepare you for the future. The skills you learn here can also help you deal with younger brothers and sisters, nieces and nephews, stepchildren, and other children who are part of your life.

Making a Commitment

Besides impressing the parole board, list at least three other reasons you want to become the best mother you can be.

____

____

____

____

____

I hereby promise to work as hard as I can to learn to become the best mom I can be.

Sign your name here: ______________________________ Date: ____________

Ground Rules

This program runs for _____ weeks. The leader of your group will inform you about the length and times the group will meet.

In a group setting, establishing ground rules is vital. For example, each woman must honor confidentiality. This means not revealing or telling others what you have heard about them. You will sign a contract on page ix that states you understand this idea and must keep to it. The counselor or group leader also must keep your statements confidential—not tell others—except (according to state law) if you threaten to harm another person or yourself or if you report instances of child abuse.

Other group rules include issues of attendance and discharges. Attendance at all classes is necessary to profit from this program. You will not be allowed to continue in the class if you miss too many sessions or repeatedly arrive late. You will discuss these ground rules and sign another form (page x) indicating that you understand them and will go along with them.

Your progress in the program will be judged in the following ways:

- Your attitude toward class and treatment as shown by your upbeat participation in discussions
- Your attendance and punctuality (being on time)
- Your completion of assignments on time
- Your interaction with the group as shown by positive comments and encouragement of others
- Your use of appropriate language by not cursing and not using racial or ethic slurs or put-downs
- Your showing of caring for others as seen in your comments
- Your making fewer attempts to control others by raising your voice, not allowing others to talk, or judging other's feelings and ideas
- Your acceptance of personal responsibility for your behavior as shown in your comments and assignments
- Other items as described by your group leader.

Group Contract

Agreement to Confidentiality

Generally, the things you hear and the things you say during group sessions are legally confidential. The group leader needs your permission to disclose information. However, the leader can give information to authorities if you are a danger to yourself (suicidal) or to others. If you threaten anyone, the leader can report that information. The leader will notify the person threatened and law enforcement. Some states also require professionals to pass on any reports of child abuse to the appropriate authorities. Everyone should honor the confidentiality of the group, but individuals should understand that the leader cannot always completely control or guarantee confidentiality in a group setting.

Absences and Tardiness

If you are absent more than ____ times, you may be dropped from the program. Being tardy too many times also may result in your being asked to leave the group.

Completion

1. You will receive a completion certificate at the end of the program if you have done all the exercises and participated in the discussion. This means you have made satisfactory progress, and you have completed all the requirements of the contract.

2. If you are transferred or move, you will be given credit for the number of classes completed if you have made successful progress.

3. If you violate the contract or any legal requirements, you will receive an Unsuccessful Discharge.

4. Please add other discharge conditions for your particular program:

____

____

____

____

Group Expectations

The group leader will discuss his/her expectations with group members. You must comply with the following rules or you may be discharged from the group:

- Respect confidentiality—no revealing identities of other group members or giving information that could identify them to other people.
- No violence will be tolerated. Violence is grounds for immediate discharge.
- No alcohol or drug use.
- No cursing.
- No racial, ethnic, sexual, religious-based, or any cutting remarks toward others.
- You must be able to admit to past mistakes.
- You must not use controlling or threatening behaviors to make the group go the way you want.
- Discussions must focus on the lesson's theme and treatment goals and not wander to other things.
- Other ____

I agree to all of the above requirements and agree to provide any Releases of Information to those with whom I agree to share information. I have read and understand this contract. I am aware that care and treatment in this area of human services is not an exact science. No one guaranteed me that I will magically improve by taking this class, but I will give it my best shot.

______________________________ ____________________

Participant's Signature Date

Chapter 1

Overcoming Barriers to Becoming a Responsible Mother

This chapter has five lessons to help you become a responsible mother. Before you learn the skills to be an effective mother, you must have the right attitude. You also must deal with past trauma, experiences, and your feelings about motherhood.

The first lesson defines "responsible motherhood." Following lessons encourage you to look at your beliefs about motherhood. You also will be asked to come to terms with your past, your own mother, and other childhood experiences. Lesson four concerns common fears and frustrations of inmate moms. This chapter ends with a lesson on what you should tell your children about your incarceration.

As you begin, remember your promise to do the best you can for your children. Good luck in this worthwhile project!

Illustration by Elizabeth Miklosovic, *The Kiss*

Lesson 1-1: Being a Responsible Mother

What is a Responsible Mother?

A responsible mother is the type of mother who all children need. Whether in prison or out, she meets her responsibilities as a parent. She will do whatever is necessary to take care of her children within the limits of the law. A responsible mother respects herself. She will do what it takes to protect her children. She never uses her children or family as an excuse for her own inappropriate or illegal behavior. She is the best mother she can be.

A responsible mother is not perfect. She has made mistakes in her life. She freely admits to her mistakes. She is determined to be there for her kids. She wants to learn how to be a more effective mother. She is willing to work hard to gain the attitudes and skills so that she can meet the needs of her children. She knows she is very important to her children. She learns all she can about how children grow so that she can be a good parent.

A responsible mother places her children's needs over her own comfort and convenience. She is alert to any danger to her children. She constantly protects her children from any possible mistreatment. She will not remain in a relationship, even with someone she loves, if she feels her children are suffering. Her eyes are always wide open.

A responsible mother is honest with her kids. She accepts responsibility and models this for her children.

A responsible mother fearlessly examines her past. This includes abuses she has suffered, and her relationship with her own mother and other family members. She is not afraid to look at both the good and bad experiences she had as a child. She uses this learning to become a better mother.

A responsible mother never abuses her children. She never punishes her children out of anger or sheer frustration. A responsible mother never hits her children or uses violence.

A responsible mother is always ready to listen and tries to understand how her kids feel, even when it is hard or inconvenient. Even if she is in jail or prison, a responsible mother puts the needs of her kids ahead of her own desires. She is fair, kind, and affectionate.

Voices and Viewpoints

Denise is always shooting her mouth off about what a great mom she is, but she was never around when her kids needed her, and now she doesn't even write or visit with them.

Brittany says, "What Denise does is her own business. But I do not think what she is doing is right. A lot of women in here get real sentimental about their kids, but they just do not bother to put out for them. That's what being a mom is."

What do you think? Is Denise a responsible mother? Is Brittany right or wrong?

____

____

____

____

____

____

____

A responsible mother makes sure she is there when her kids need her. She spends time with her kids—even when there are other things she would rather do. She listens to her children and takes them seriously.

A responsible mother provides for her children. She makes sure that they have food, shelter, and the other things they need. A responsible mother works hard to be independent so she can provide for her kids.

A responsible mother loves her kids enough to make rules and set limits. She tells them what behaviors are acceptable and what things they should not do. She shares her values and family and cultural traditions with her children. She takes her share of responsibility for disciplining her children.

A responsible mother makes sure that her kids are safe and healthy. She sees to it that they eat right. She makes sure that they are safe from abuse and physical harm. She makes sure they get the right health care. She takes them to the doctor and dentist when they need to go.

A responsible mother would never do anything that would put her children in harm's way. She is very careful not to do anything that might cause her to be separated from her children again. She avoids drugs and alcohol, which might prevent her from using her best judgment. She is also careful about the people she chooses as friends or associates. She does not think about her own comfort or needs first. She does not base her decisions on how they will make her feel. She makes decisions that are best for her kids. She never uses her kids or family as an excuse for any of her behaviors or decisions.

Exercise 1-1a: Responsible Mother or Not?

Directions: Carefully read each question below and circle the best answer.

1. Does a responsible mother believe that her kids need her in their life? Yes No

2. Does a responsible mother believe that her kids are better off without her? Yes No

3. Does a responsible mother respect herself? Yes No

4. Does a responsible mother run away when things get tough? Yes No

5. Does a responsible mother always make the right decisions when it comes to her kids? Yes No

6. Does a responsible mother learn from her mistakes? Yes No

7. Does a responsible mother love her kids so much that she avoids visits with them because it is too hard to leave them? Yes No

8. Can you be a responsible mother if your own mom wasn't one? Yes No

9. Is becoming a responsible mother entirely up to you? Yes No

Exercise 1-1b: Characteristics of a Responsible Mother

Directions: Read each of the following questions and write in your best answer.

1. What are three things that a responsible mother would do with her kids?

   (1) ____

   ____

   ____

   ____

   (2) ____

   ____

   ____

   ____

   (3) ____

   ____

   ____

   ____

2. What are three things a responsible mother would never do?

   (1) ____

   ____

   ____

   ____

(2) ____

____

____

____

(3) ____

____

____

____

3. What are three things a responsible mother in prison can do for her children?

(1) ____

____

____

____

(2) ____

____

____

____

(3) ____

____

____

____

Lesson 1-2: Irrational Beliefs about Motherhood

The Importance of Self-Talk

Most people think by silently talking to themselves. We call these thoughts *self-talk*. Your thoughts lead to your behavior. They also control how you feel about things. Some thoughts lead to helpful behavior and pleasant feelings. Others can lead to bad feelings and self-destructive behavior.

Even if you are not aware of it, your thoughts are always in the background. They shape what you do and how you feel. Most people put these thoughts into words and sentences. We have inner chats with ourselves all the time. Occasionally, people think in pictures.

Albert Ellis, a psychologist, said that thoughts that lead to unwanted behavior and bad feelings are irrational—they do not make sense. They are not worth having. Some people in self-help groups call these thoughts "stinking thinking." People can avoid very bad feelings and unwanted behavior by changing their thinking.

What is Rational Thinking?

Rational thinking is having thoughts that lead to good behaviors and feelings. Life, however, is filled with unpleasant and disappointing things. No one has a guarantee that he or she will avoid these things. The opposite of rational thinking is irrational thinking. Irrational thinking makes bad things even worse. Irrational thinking turns disappointment into disaster. Irrational thinking turns irritation into violent anger. Learning how to think rationally helps you avoid the very bad feelings and behaviors that get you into trouble.

What are Irrational Thoughts?

How can you tell if your thinking is irrational? When we have irrational ideas, they often are demands about things we cannot control. The main thing we cannot control is how other people act. Irrational thoughts have certain words and phrases in them such as: "*must*," "*should*," "*ought to*," and "*have to*." Irrational thoughts may have very strong words in them. These are words such as "*awful*," "*terrible*," "*catastrophe*," "*unbearable*," and "*can't stand it*." When you use any of these words, be careful. You may not be thinking rationally.

Voices and Viewpoints

Shanice says, "There are times when you just cannot control your feelings. I mean other people really make me mad. I just can't help it. When my kids ignore me, I have to feel really bad about that. I know my mother is always saying bad things about me. I just can't get that out of my mind."

Estella says, "I do not like the idea that other people can control the way I feel. I should be in charge of my own feelings. If I get mad, it's because I want to, not because someone made me. Sure, it hurts when I think about not seeing my kids, but why make it worse by whining about it? It is hard enough just not seeing them. I figure I should cut my losses and not hurt myself more by thinking a bunch of trash."

What do you think? Who controls your feelings?

____

____

____

Occasionally, some irrational thoughts keep you from doing something. Self-talk that stops you is full of words such as the following: *"I can't," "too hard," "too difficult,"* and *"impossible."*

Questions often hide irrational demands. When you say to yourself, "Why did this happen to me?" that is the same as saying, "This *should not* have happened to me." If you say, "Why did she do that?" you really are saying: "She *should not* have done that." Be careful about asking yourself questions that really are irrational. You can learn to be aware of your irrational thoughts so that you can change them. Rational thinking allows you to control your behavior and feelings better.

Here are some examples of common irrational thoughts. Note the words in bold type. These words are your hints that these thoughts are not rational.

1. Other people **must always** love and approve of me or it's **awful**.
2. **I must always** be **perfect** in **everything** I do.

3. Other people are **extremely wicked** and **should be severely** punished for their behavior.
4. If things do not go the way I think they **should**, it is **awful**, and **terrible**, and **I can't stand it**.
5. If something might be dangerous, **I have to constantly** think about it and feel **very upset** about it.
6. I just **can't do** it, so **I shouldn't** even try.
7. Why does she always do that? (This is the irrational demand "She **shouldn't** do that" disguised as a question.)

These types of thoughts get people into trouble. If you constantly say these things to yourself, you will feel depressed, angry, or worried. Apply the following four tests for rational thinking to detect irrational thoughts. Ask yourself the following questions:

Tests for Rational Thinking

1. Is what I am thinking really true?
2. Does what I am thinking help me get what I want?
3. Does what I am thinking keep me out of fights?
4. Does what I am thinking keep me from feeling bad?

If a thought does not pass any of these tests, it is not rational. If it is not rational, it is not worth having. It can only hurt you.

Changing Irrational Beliefs: Disagree and Change

After you spot an irrational thought, how can you change it? The first step is to argue with the thought. You tell yourself, "No, this is not right." We call this disagreeing with the thought. The second step is to change the thought into one that is more helpful. The two basic steps in getting rid of an irrational thought are the following:

1. Disagree: Make your best argument against the thought.
2. Change: Change the thought so that it makes sense and is helpful.

Let's change the irrational thought listed below:

"Other people must always love and approve of me or it's awful."

Step 1. Disagree: If a thought like this is running through your head, the first step is to argue with it. You might say something like:

"No, this is simply not true. There is no rule of the universe that other people must always love and approve of me. That is simply a wish of mine. Also, it is not awful if they do not love me. It is hard, it is upsetting, it is disappointing, but it is something I can live with."

Step 2. Change: In this step, change the irrational belief into a more rational one. This involves changing the extreme language and irrational words. An example would be as follows:

"It would be nice if other people always approve of me and understand me and agree with me, but I have no guarantee that this will happen. I cannot control other people's behavior. This is just something I would like that would make things easier. When it doesn't happen, I might feel some hurt and disappointment. But I can survive it."

You can change irrational thoughts in many different ways. The most important thing is to develop more healthy self-talk. Healthy self-talk does not get rid of unpleasant experiences. It can help you manage them better. Rational self-talk can turn painful depression into manageable disappointment. It can turn crippling fear into reasonable caution. It can turn explosive anger into controllable irritation.

Personal Irrational Beliefs and Irrational Beliefs about Motherhood

In addition to the basic irrational beliefs discussed above, many women have their own special set of irrational beliefs. Some common irrational beliefs revolve around the following themes:

1. Feeling sorry for yourself
2. Blaming others for your current behavior and feelings
3. Convincing yourself that you are unable to do something
4. Making a big deal over an unwanted event
5. Demanding that other people treat you better

If you find yourself listening to such self-talk, stop and think. Then, use the two-step process (Disagree and Change) to alter this self-talk. Pages 12 and 13 provide some common irrational beliefs about motherhood. Along with each belief is an example of how you can use the two-step process to change this irrational belief into something more helpful.

1. Because I messed up in the past, my kids are better off without me.

Disagree: *There is no reason to think that my kids will be better off without me. In fact, most people believe that having a mother is very important for children.*

Changed: *I admit I messed up in the past. Now, I'm determined to do better in the future for the sake of my kids. Mothers are important to kids.*

2. This parenting stuff is just too hard for me to learn; I just can't do it.

Disagree: *Even though studying this stuff may be hard work at times, this is something that I can do. It may not be fun or easy, but I can do it.*

Changed: *Learning about being a good mother is hard work. But, this only helps me try harder. I do not have to be perfect at it.*

3. Because I was hurt terribly in the past, I must feel angry and upset about this for the rest of my life.

Disagree: *Although my mother hurt me in the past, how I feel now is my own decision. There is no reason why I should allow bad events from the past to continue to hurt me. I have been hurt enough.*

Changed: *My mother mistreated me and I do not like it. I'm determined not to let that continue to stir up bad feelings now that I am an adult.*

4. I have to be perfect in everything I do with my children.

Disagree: *I am just a human being and cannot be perfect. I will make some mistakes with my children sooner or later. I do not have to feel terrible about it.*

Changed: *It is disappointing not to be perfect. I will continue to try to do the best I can regarding my children. If I make a mistake, I will learn from it. The important thing is that I am trying.*

5. My kids must always love and respect me, or I'm a terrible mother.

Disagree: *There is no reason why my kids must love and respect me at all times. It would be great if they did. However, my kids are just human, and sometimes they do not do the right thing. There are times when children do not show love and respect to the best of mothers.*

Changed: *I would like my kids to show me love and respect. If they do not, I can live with this. It does not mean that I'm a terrible mother. Sometimes, they will say childish things in anger that they do not mean. I am strong enough to ignore it.*

It is very important for mothers to learn how to change self-defeating beliefs into more helpful thoughts. By doing this, you will have less irrational self-talk. Think of it as learning how to change channels on a radio. If you heard someone repeating painful irritating thoughts over and over again on the radio, you would quickly change stations. If you are not sure whether a belief is rational, use the four tests for rational thinking (page 10). Asking these four questions can quickly tell you if a thought is irrational.

Exercise 1-2: Developing Rational Beliefs about Motherhood

Directions: For each irrational belief below, write your disagreement (argument against the self-talk) and a revision (the changed self-talk, which is more helpful).

Example: Irrational belief: "I must be perfect in everything I do with my kids. If I'm not perfect, I am worthless."

Disagreement: I am just a human being, so I will make mistakes. Being perfect is just a foolish demand that doesn't help me or my kids in any way. Instead, it makes me feel bad about myself. Who needs that?

Changed: While I do not like mistakes, there's no way I can be perfect. It would be better if I try to learn from my mistakes. I do not need to blame myself. Blaming myself doesn't help my kids, it only makes me feel bad. I will just try to do better next time.

1. **Irrational belief:** I just cannot work with my relatives who take care of my kids. So, I should never see my kids again.

Disagreement: ____

____

____

____

____

Changed: ____

____

____

____

____

2. **Irrational belief:** I must be too stupid to be a good mom. I just can't do it.

Disagreement: ____

____

____

____

____

Changed: ____

____

____

____

____

3. **Irrational belief:** If I cannot have my children with me at all times, it is awful and I can't stand it.

Disagreement: ____

____

____

____

____

Changed: ____

____

____

____

____

4. **Irrational belief:** Because other people messed me up, I'm doomed to mess up my kids.

Disagreement: ______________________________

____

____

____

____

Changed: ______________________________

____

____

____

____

5. **Irrational belief:** When things do not go the way I want them to, it's awful and terrible, and I can't stand it.

Disagreement: ______________________________

____

____

____

____

Changed: ______________________________

____

____

____

____

6. **Irrational belief:** I cannot be responsible for my kids by myself. I have to have a man to help me.

Disagreement: ____

____

____

____

____

Changed: ____

____

____

____

____

7. **Irrational belief:** Since I am in prison and cannot be with my kids, there is nothing I can do for them now. So, it is best to just not think about it.

Disagreement: ____

____

____

____

____

Changed: ____

____

____

____

____

Lesson 1-3: Coming to Terms with Your Past

Like Mother Like Daughter?

Most women learn how to be mothers by acting like their own mothers. If their mother yelled at them or beat them, many believe that is the way mothers should act. Some women may punish their children all the time because their mothers were very harsh.

Other women, especially those who are angry at their mothers, may choose to be the exact opposite. These women may not discipline their children or set any limits for them at all. They may spoil their kids by buying them expensive things they do not need.

Your feelings about your own mother are important because they have a lot to do with how you will treat your children. If you were lucky enough to have a responsible mother, you know that she was always there for you. You know that she provided for you and that she loved you.

Many women were not raised by their parents. Relatives, such as grandmothers or aunts, may have raised them, or they may have been raised in foster homes. These women may have never known their mothers at all. The women who they knew as children may not have been good models.

Even if your mom was never there to protect you or teach you, you still can learn from her. Even if you had terrible experiences as a child, you now can use those experiences in a good way. First, you can learn what things not to do. You can also use your bad memories as encouragement in trying to do a better job with your own children.

Many women did not have responsible mothers. They had mothers who were self-centered, unpredictable, or absent. Your mother may not have been there for you in the way you needed her to be. She did not protect you. Maybe she was sick, troubled, or just weak. It does not matter why. Some women spend much of their lives asking why. They make themselves angry or sad because their mom couldn't cut it.

Some women ask, "Why did this happen to me?" When you ask this, remember you are not really asking a question. Instead, you are making an irrational demand—the demand that your mother not be the way she was. You really are saying "My mom should not have been such a bad mother." Nobody is born with a guarantee she will get the best kind of mother. A big part of being an adult is being mature enough to accept facts. One of the hardest facts to accept is that your mother may not have been what you wanted her to be.

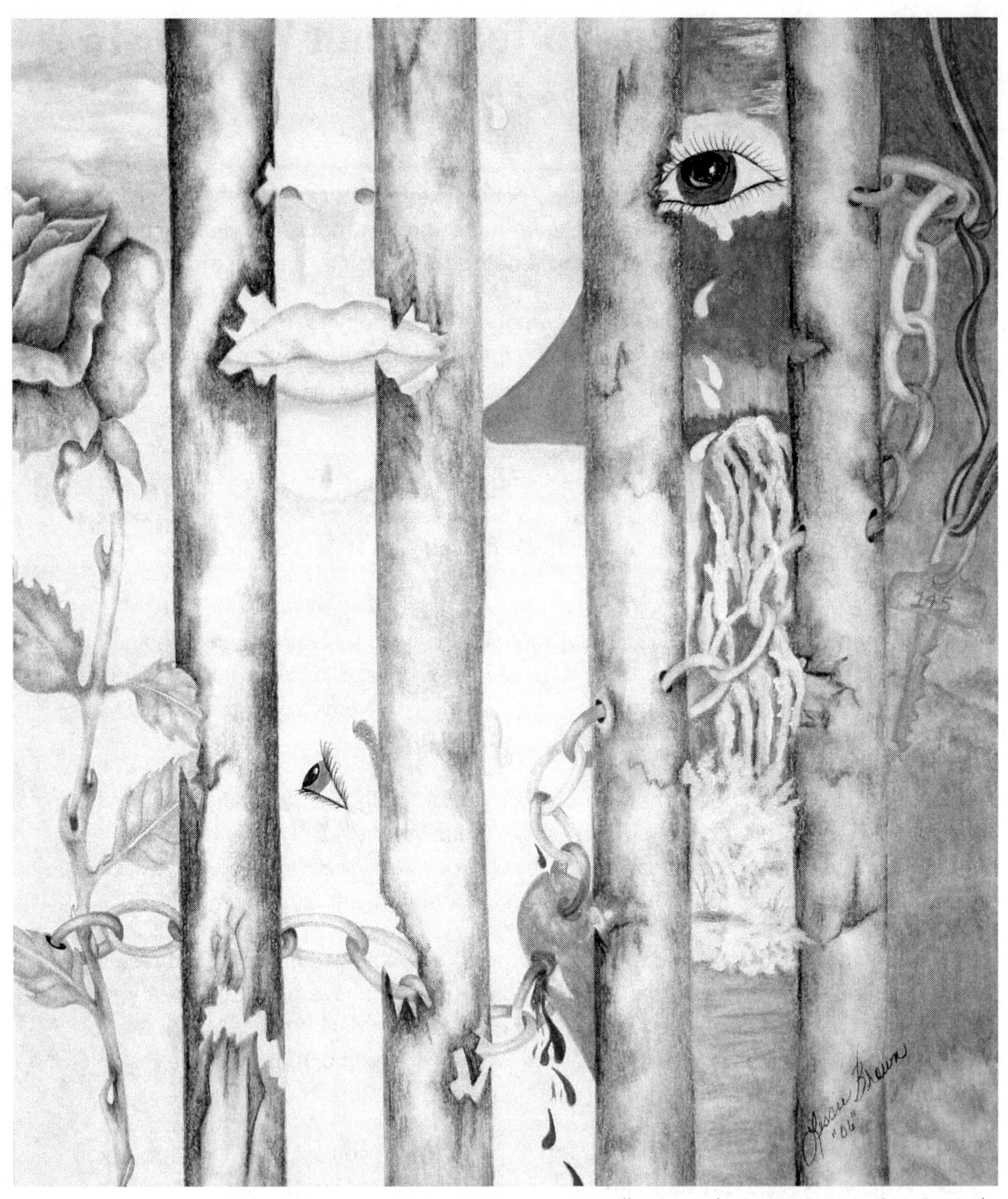

Illustration by Lessie Brown, *3 xs Denied*

Abuse and Past Trauma

Many women who are incarcerated have long histories of being abused—emotionally, physically, and sexually. Often, such abuse is related to later problems such as depression, anxiety, and anger. It also can lead to substance abuse as a way to try to stop the bad feelings. Abuse also interferes with a woman's ability to have stable relationships. Women who were abused as children may choose men as boyfriends or husbands who also hit or hurt them.

Many of these abused women are very angry at their mothers for failing to protect them. They wonder why their mothers did not put their safety first. There is never any excuse for failing to protect a child. However, some mothers are so dependent on their abusive partner that they do not believe they could survive if they left. Others are afraid that leaving would just lead to further violence—both to the children and to themselves. Many women feel completely trapped in such relationships and are unable to see how they might free themselves. You can take action to break the cycle of abuse, but many women are too frightened to believe this.

Cultural and religious pressures may also make it difficult for some women to escape abusive relationships. You may have been taught that it is always wrong for a wife to leave her husband, even when he is hurting you or your children. It is important for you to look at some of the reasons your mother may have had for not protecting you. That way, you can develop the strengths and competencies to succeed where she failed.

Some women will need professional counseling to help them deal with the abuses of the past. Others may benefit greatly from self-help and support groups. In any case, it will take a great deal of courage to face your past traumas, learn from them, and move on with your life.

Using Your Experiences Wisely

You do not have to forgive your mother. There is no reason to forget what happened. However, there is every reason to stop letting your thoughts and memories hurt you now that you are an adult. You can stop the hurt by not demanding that the past be different. You can do this by reaching inside for the courage to face and accept what really happened.

Some mothers feel overwhelmed by anger and fear. They see the world as such a terrible place that no one can do anything to protect them against hurt and disaster. However, as an adult, you can look at yourself and decide, "What kind of person do I want to be? Do I constantly want to be negative and critical? Do I want to say hurtful things in anger? Do I want to tell my daughters that women cannot handle things alone? Am I prepared to break old patterns?

"Can I listen to my children, respect their feelings, and encourage them in their efforts? Can I set a new goal to present myself as a competent adult? Can I be a person who problem solves when I make mistakes? And finally, can I commit myself to never stopping to work toward a better future for my children and myself?"

Voices and Viewpoints

Rita says, "I never knew my mother. She split when I was just a baby. She left my grandmother to raise all five kids. Other kids teased me because I didn't have a mother. I got into lots of fights. Sometimes I would lie. I would tell people my mother was on the road with a band as a singer. I would imagine what she was like, and then I would hate her for leaving. I wondered if there was something wrong with me. Maybe she left because I was bad. I wanted to have a mother to love me more than anything."

Eunice says, "You had it easy. I wish my mother would have left. She was there, but she was always high. When she was drugged up, she would bring home men who would mess with me and my little sisters. I hated her for what she did to us. I was glad when she died. I do not hate her so much anymore. I just think she was messed up."

Who do you think had a tougher time growing up, Rita or Eunice? Why?

____

____

____

Do you think it is better to have a mother even if she is not a very good one? Why?

____

____

____

In the past, our culture taught people that the job of the father was to provide for and protect the family. Fathers were to discipline the children. Women were supposed to raise children and provide affection. The grandmother was supposed to help and give advice. Things have changed, and this traditional arrangement no longer applies. Today, many women raise children alone and often carry the entire burden themselves. Today's mother has to be independent and self-sufficient.

The Bad News and the Good News

The bad news is that your childhood may have been very painful. The good news—that part of your life is over—forever. The even better news is that you are in control of what happens to your children. Some people have the irrational idea that because bad things happened to them as children, such experiences must cause problems for the rest of their lives. This is simply untrue. We can learn from such things to make sure we do not let them happen to our children. Learning to use the memories of your own mother can help you be a better mother. You can use the good things and learn from the bad.

Exercise 1-3a: My Mother

Directions: Answer these questions about your mother. If your mother was not around while you were growing up, answer these questions about some other woman in your life—stepmom, grandmother, aunt, or other woman. If there was no one else, imagine what your mother would have been like, and answer the questions about the mother you imagined:

1. Do you think (imagine) your mom was a responsible mother? Give reasons why you think that.

    ____

    ____

    ____

    ____

2. What type of effect do you think (imagine) your mom had on your life?

3. How do you think your mother learned to be a mom? Who taught her?

Exercise 1-3b: My Mother and Me

Directions: If your mother was not around or if you never knew her, complete the following about some other woman in your life. If there was no one else around, use your imagination and describe what your mother could have been like.

1. What sort of things were (would have been) most important to your mother?

2. What things are most important to you?

3. What sort of things do you want to be important to your children?

4. In what ways are you like your mother?

5. In what ways are you different from your mother?

6. What is your best memory of your mother (or what memory would you like to have had about your mother)?

7. What is the worst memory of your mother that you can remember or imagine?

____

____

____

____

8. Do you think that you were able to please your mother?

____

____

____

____

9. How do you imagine your grandmother treated your mother?

____

____

____

____

10. Who do you imagine were your mother's heroines? Who are yours?

____

____

____

____

11. In what ways does your mother shape the way you feel and behave today?

12. What are some unhelpful thoughts that you have had about your mother?

13. As an adult, what can you realistically say about your mother?

14. If your mother were in front of you right now, what are some things you would like to say to her?

15. What could you tell yourself right now (rational self-talk) that would help you learn from your mother's mistakes?

____

____

____

____

Exercise 1-3c: My Mother as a Parent

Directions: If your mother was not around or you never knew her, complete the following about any other woman who was around. If there was no one else, use your imagination and describe what your mother could have been like.

1. Overall, do you think your mother was a good model or a bad model as a parent? Why?

____

____

____

____

2. What were the worst things she did as a mother?

____

____

____

____

3. What were the best things she did as a mother?

4. What can you learn from your mother about being a parent?

5. When you think about her, what feelings do you have about your mother right now?

6. How can you use the feelings you have toward your mother to be a better mother?

Exercise 1-3d: Growing Up Without a Mother

Directions: This exercise is only for women who grew up with no mother at home. If your mother was present in your home when you were growing up, skip this exercise. If not, read the questions below and provide your best answers.

1. Since there was no mother in your home, where did you get your ideas about what a mother should be like?

   ____

   ____

   ____

   ____

2. How did growing up without a mother affect your ability to be a responsible mother?

   ____

   ____

   ____

   ____

3. When you were little, what feelings did you have about not having a mother? Have those feelings changed?

   ____

   ____

   ____

   ____

4. If you were raised primarily by a grandmother or other relatives, what did they teach you about being a mother? What didn't they teach you?

5. How would your life have been different if you had had a mother in your home?

Exercise 1-3e: Coping with Abuse and Trauma

Directions: This exercise is for women who experienced abuse as a child. It will take courage to answer some of these questions.

1. What feelings did you have about the abuse as a child? Have these feelings changed now that you are an adult?

2. What feelings do you have toward your mother about the abuse? How do you feel about her failure to protect you?

____

____

____

____

3. Do you completely understand that abuse is never, ever the victim's fault in any way? Why is this true?

____

____

____

____

4. If they were in front of you right now, what would you say to your abuser(s)?

____

____

____

____

5. As a mother and an adult now, what advice would you give to that little girl (who was you) about the abuse she experienced?

____

____

____

____

Lesson 1-4: Fears and Frustrations of Incarcerated Mothers

Fears of Mothers

All mothers worry about their children. That goes with the territory. Mothers worry about doing the right thing. They worry about how their actions will affect their children in the future. They worry about making mistakes. They also fear their children will have a difficult life and not grow up happy. Moms are also concerned about the health of their children. Having a sick child can be one of the most frightening things in a mother's life.

Incarcerated mothers often have additional fears for their children. We describe some of these below. As you read through these items, check any concerns you have thought about.

❑ Fear of Loss

The major fear of most incarcerated mothers is losing contact with their children forever. Being separated from their children is very difficult for most mothers. Some incarcerated mothers may put off visits because they do not want to deal with the hurt of repeated separations. Many incarcerated mothers fear they will lose custody of their children and never see them again.

❑ Fear of Rejection

Incarcerated mothers may fear that their children will come to hate and reject them. They may worry that other people will turn the children against them, and the children will think they are bad.

❑ Fear of Being Forgotten

Many women are afraid that their children will forget them. Incarceration often means long separations and limited contact. The thought that they might be wiped from their children's memory is very hurtful for most mothers.

❑ Fear that Another Woman Will Steal Their Child

Some mothers fear their children will bond with another woman while they are incarcerated. This can be especially upsetting if there is a dominant stepmother,

mother-in-law, grandmother, or other caretaker in the picture. Many women may feel angry that some other woman may "steal" their children. They may feel very jealous. Confused and frustrated, they often feel there is nothing they can do to keep from losing their children.

❑ The Fear of Being Powerless to Help

Most incarcerated mothers find not being able to do anything to help their children is extremely frustrating. The painful feeling of not being able to do anything attacks self-esteem. Many women start to feel as if they are useless and worthless.

❑ Fear of Having Harmed the Child

Many mothers fear their incarceration will permanently damage their children. They feel that because of their actions, their children will never have a successful life. Because they are ashamed, they may start to believe their child would be better off without them. Due to this feeling, they may run away from their children. They also may fear that their children will turn out just like them and end up incarcerated, too.

Voices and Viewpoints

Dorothy says, "One of the reasons that I do not like to have much contact with my kids is that I just can't stand it when they tell me about something they need or some problem they have and there is absolutely nothing I can do to help. I would rather just not hear about it. It just makes me feel so worthless."

What do you think about Dorothy's complaint? Is it reasonable? Who does she seem most concerned about?

____

____

____

____

____

Incarceration does put many pressures on children. Fortunately, most children are quite tough. Know and face these fears—some of them may be partly true. Even if they are true, feeling upset or depressed about them will not help your children or you. Use these fears positively to motivate you to work at becoming a better mother.

Managing Your Fears and Frustrations

Like other unwanted feelings, fears come from irrational self-talk. By arguing against this irrational self-talk and changing these beliefs, you can learn to manage these fears. The main irrational belief that causes fear is this idea:

"If it's possible that something bad might happen, I should worry about it constantly."

You can see that this is an irrational belief. It does not help get you what you want. It does not help you avoid emotional upset or fights. It is simply not true. What are some rational reasons that you should worry about it constantly? There are none. Worry never prevents bad things from happening. Worry just keeps you feeling upset in the meantime. A more helpful thing to say to yourself might be the following:

"If it's possible that something bad might happen, it would be best to do whatever I can to prevent it. I can work best if I keep myself calm."

To manage your fears and frustration, you must find the harmful self-talk and then use the "Disagree and Change" technique to change it into something more helpful.

Exercise 1-4: Managing Fears and Frustration

Directions: Complete the following:

1. List the three biggest fears you have about your children.

   ____

   ____

   ____

2. What are some things you can do to reduce or get rid of these fears?

____

____

____

3. Consider this belief:

   If my child hates me because I was sent to prison, it will be the end of the world, and I won't be able to stand it.

   How is this statement untrue, and how could it cause you problems?

____

____

____

   What would be a better thing to tell yourself instead?

____

____

____

4. Consider this belief:

   If my child becomes attached to some other woman while I am away, it would make me feel very, very angry.

   Why is this statement unhelpful and irrational?

____

____

____

What would be a better thing to tell yourself instead?

____

____

____

Instead of keeping yourself upset and angry, what would be a better thing to do?

____

____

____

5. Consider this belief:

   I worry day and night that if my ex-husband gets custody of my children, I might never be able to see them again. This makes me so upset that I cannot think straight.

   How is this statement untrue and how could it cause you problems?

   ____

   ____

   ____

   What would be a better and more helpful thing to tell yourself?

   ____

   ____

   ____

   Instead of keeping yourself upset and worried, what would be a better thing to do?

   ____

   ____

   ____

Lesson 1-5: Overcoming Shame and Guilt: What Do I Tell My Kids?

How Do I Tell My Children?

If your children do not know about your incarceration, it is important to develop a plan to tell them as soon as possible. Make the plan in cooperation with the child's current caretaker. It is better for children to learn this from a family member. You do not want them to hear about it on the playground. It is best to keep the explanation direct and simple.

Make the following points in your explanation to the child:

1. You still love and care for the child.
2. The incarceration is not the child's fault.
3. You did something wrong and have to take a punishment.
4. You will be separated from the family for a while (give some idea of how long it will be).
5. While you are away, the child will be taken care of and will be safe.
6. You will keep yourself safe.
7. Being in prison or jail is not something that makes you a hero or cool.
8. Tell the child what your daily life is like. This decreases their fear. Give your child specific details about your daily activities such as the work you do, classes you attend, exercise, recreation, commissary activity, and other things.
9. If you wish to keep the incarceration private, tell the child something he can tell others, such as "My parents are separated right now," or simply "My mother doesn't live at home anymore."
10. Tell the child if there will there be phone calls, letters, visits, or other contacts.
11. Emphasize that you are not "bad," but that you made mistakes and now must take responsibility.

As you can see, telling your children about being incarcerated takes careful planning. Children need to know the truth. They do not always need all the painful details. They are seeking a way to make sense out of what happened. Keep the way you explain things to younger children simple. For example say, "Mommy broke a rule." "Mommy

Voices and Viewpoints

Jada says, "I'm not telling my kids nothing. If they find out what I did, they're just going to hate me. They'll tell my mother, and she'll use it against me. They are better off not knowing anything about what happened."

What you think about this decision? Is it reasonable? What would you suggest?

____

____

____

____

____

____

took some medicine she should not have taken." or "Mommy took something that didn't belong to her."

Older children can handle a more complete story. Remember, the truth is often better than what the children might imagine. Sometimes you might be tempted not to tell the children about your incarceration. This usually is not a good idea. They may feel betrayed when they find out the truth.

Handling Questions from Your Child

It is a good thing if your children have questions. Encourage your children to ask questions. It shows that the children are trying to handle the situation. Answers may ease some of the worry they feel. Depending on their age, children will have many different questions about incarceration. The questions may come all at once or they may come over the course of several weeks. Again, it is best to be truthful, but do not provide unnecessary details. Remember, it is usually better to say you do not know and try to find the right answer, than to give the wrong information.

The following are common questions that children have about an incarcerated mother. Be ready to answer these questions.

1. Is my mommy safe?
2. Is it my fault?
3. Who will take care of me?
4. Why must Mommy be away?
5. What is Mommy doing right now?
6. When will I get to see Mommy again?
7. What does Mommy do all day?
8. Is Mommy bad?

Answer these questions directly. Even when children have been told the whole story, they may ask some questions again and again. They may ask many of these questions once more after reunification.

Repeated questions suggest that the child is having problems accepting certain things. Some children need time to adapt to the situation of an incarcerated mother. At first, they may not want to discuss the issue at all. They even may refuse to talk about it. These children need to be given time and support.

Children often feel abandoned and express sadness and anger. It is best to be ready for possible rejection by your child. Some children may act like younger children, wetting the bed or throwing tantrums. Such reactions are normal. It takes time to work through these intense feelings. Professional counseling (often available through school, church, or community agencies) can help them adjust to the situation. If they are given support and the help they need, they can adapt to the situation.

In talking to your children about being incarcerated, it might be useful to tell them about a typical day in your life. Start with the morning wake-up and go through the things that happen each day. You might tell about days when the schedule is different. It is important that you make it clear to your child what you are doing and how you are getting along.

However, when speaking to your children, do not speak to them as you would with another adult. Do not share all of your pain, fears, or resentments. They are too young to shoulder this burden, and need you to be upbeat, reassuring, and positive.

Difficult Subjects

You may find it hard to talk about many things. Remember, you have a choice about what things to tell your children. It is okay if you do not want to share some issues with them. You also may want to wait until the child gets older to talk about some things. You must not frighten them.

Also, remember that they may not be able to understand many things. Violence, homosexuality, risks for disease, abuse, and other threats to safety are just some of the things you must think about. Then, you can decide how much you would like to tell your children. Being honest with your children does not mean telling them everything in detail. Being honest means telling them what they need to know and being sensitive to their needs.

Exercise 1-5: What to Tell Your Children

Directions: Carefully read each question and write in your best answer.

1. Was your mother, father, or other close relative ever incarcerated? If so, how did you feel about it? (If no one in the family was incarcerated, imagine how it would feel.)

   ____

   ____

   ____

2. What sort of things do you think your children will want to know about your incarceration?

   ____

   ____

   ____

3. What things do you feel comfortable telling them?

___

___

___

4. What things do you feel you should not tell them?

___

___

___

5. What can you do if your child seems to be angry with you?

___

___

___

6. What would you tell your children if they said they wanted to go to prison, too?

___

___

___

7. What would you tell your child if she said she was afraid you will get hurt in prison?

___

___

___

8. How would you feel and what would you say if your child said she did not want to see you anymore because you are a bad person?

____

____

____

9. What things have you learned from being incarcerated that you think are important to share with your children?

____

____

____

Illustration by Kinnari Sutariya, *Wearing Blues*

Chapter 2:

Understanding Child Development

This chapter has four lessons. They describe how children grow and change from infancy to adolescence. It is important for you to know what to expect at each stage of development. This way, you can identify problems and learn how to deal with them.

You will learn how a child grows and how a child's thinking and learning change over time. You also will learn the way children learn to get along with other people and how they use language. Being able to control their feelings is another skill children will need to be successful.

Children's needs and abilities are different at each stage in a child's development. This chapter will help you identify these needs and tasks. You will learn what you can do to help your child develop into a healthy and happy adult.

Lesson 2-1: What is Child Development?

Child Development: A Definition

Just a few hundred years ago, children were treated like little adults. In old pictures, they look just like adults, only smaller. We now know that children are very different from adults in many ways.

Children are constantly growing and changing. They are physically maturing, and the ways they think, feel, and behave change over time. Just as a basketball game is divided in periods, we can divide childhood into blocks of time called "stages." The age of the children and their physical, mental, language, emotional, and social features determine their stage of development. The first stage of childhood is infancy, and the last stage is adolescence.

We call this overall process of change over time "development." Every mother needs to understand how her children grow and change. Women who have had a lot of contact with children may have reached many of these conclusions on their own.

Why is Understanding Child Development Important?

The main reason to understand child development is so that you can have realistic expectations for your children. If expectations are too high, you might feel frustrated, angry, or disappointed. For example, some parents begin toilet training their child far too early, long before the child is ready. These parents are bound to be frustrated. Some mothers might get angry at their children. They may punish them for "not trying hard enough" or for "disobeying." In extreme cases, a very frustrated mother may physically abuse a child. Other mothers may feel so disappointed that they think something is wrong with their child and reject him or her.

If your expectations are too low, you might not give your child enough challenges and opportunities. For example, if parents continue to hand feed children long after they are able to use a spoon, it may prevent the child from gaining coordination and feeling independent.

Another reason why it is important to understand child development is so that you can learn various methods of discipline to be used at different stages of development. Discipline is the way that you correct and teach your child. Discipline is not just punishment. Discipline is what you do to help your child learn how to follow rules. If you choose a method that is not right for the child's developmental stage, chances are it will not work well. A bad choice probably will end up frustrating both you and the child.

As children go through different stages, they have different needs. For example, an infant may need a lot of holding and close contact, while a toddler needs the freedom to run around. At each stage, the child's fears, interests, and ways of understanding the world are different. However, each child is an individual, and "normal" covers a wide range.

Stages of Child Development

We can divide childhood into four stages:

1. Infancy and Toddlerhood (0-3 years)
2. Early Childhood (4-6 years)
3. Childhood (7-11 years)
4. Adolescence (12+ years)

In other lessons in this chapter, we will look at children in each of these four stages. We will look at the different aspects of their development, including:

- Physical and motor development: how the child grows and learns to move
- Mental and language development: how the child's thinking, learning, and speaking change over time
- Social and emotional development: how the child gets along with other people and expresses feelings

Do All Children Behave the Same Way in Each Stage?

No! All children do not behave the same way in each stage. Children go through similar stages, but each child develops at a different speed or rate and in a slightly different way. Children may not show all the traits of every stage. It is not unusual for a child to lag behind in some features or to jump ahead in others. For instance, a child may walk early, but then be late in talking. Mothers cannot always depend on age to decide what stage of development their children are going through. They must figure out the stage based on the children's behavior (what the children are actually doing).

Voices and Viewpoints

Carla says, "I do not need to know all this 'development' stuff about kids. My mom never knew this and she raised six kids just fine. I say you just treat them all the same."

Fern says, "I do not know much about this, but I need to know more about kids. I want to make sure that I'm doing the right thing. I want my kids to have a better chance than I did."

What do you think? How important is it for you to know how your kids grow and change?

____

____

____

____

____

____

____

What Happens When There Are Big Problems in Development?

Minor problems in development are very common. Unfortunately, in some cases, children have big problems. For many reasons, children may not develop mentally or emotionally as they should. Children may have social problems and a hard time getting along with people. These severe problems are sometimes called *developmental disabilities.*

Mental retardation and autism are two major developmental disabilities. There are many other developmental disabilities. In mental retardation, the child's ability to learn is slower than other children's. In autism, the child has problems relating to people. An autistic child has social and emotional problems. These children seem to live in a separate world at times. Sometimes, autistic children do not learn to talk like other children.

Children with developmental disabilities need special help. They need this help at home and at school. These children usually qualify for special programs and services. They may get this help at schools, a clinic, or in the home. If your children have a developmental disability, your parenting plan should include ways of getting them the special help they need.

Exercise 2-1: Child Development Self-Test

Instructions: Answer each question true or false. Then, check your answers against the correct ones in the fine print.

1. Development is the process of change and growth over time. True False

   True.

2. People always thought that children were very different from adults. True False

   False. In the past, children were treated as miniature adults.

3. Mothers should learn about child development so that they know what to expect as their child grows up. True False

   True.

4. If you know what to expect, it is likely that you will feel frustrated, angry, or disappointed with your child. True False

   False. Realistic expectations can help you deal better with your child.

5. We can divide the childhood years into different periods called "stages." True False

   True.

6. You should always use the same type of discipline at every stage of development. True False

   False. Methods of discipline are very different for children of different ages and stages.

7. The child's fears, interests, and ways of understanding change at different stages of development. True False

   True. Children's outlooks on the world change quickly as they grow.

8. All children develop in the same way at exactly the same speed. True False

   False. Children grow and develop at very different rates. This is normal and to be expected.

9. Major problems in development are called *developmental disabilities.* True False

   True.

10. Mental retardation and autism are not *developmental disabilities.* True False

    False. Mental retardation and autism are major problems called developmental disabilities.

11. When children learn very slowly, especially compared to others, they may be mentally retarded. True False

    True. For example, children with moderate mental retardation generally learn half as much, half as fast as other children. But, they can and do learn things. Patience and special teaching methods help a lot.

12. Autism is a developmental disability in which the child's social, emotional, and often language abilities are not the same as those of other children. True False

    True. Children with autism have difficulty relating to other people. They often have trouble communicating with others.

13. Children with developmental disabilities do not need special education services to help them develop fully. True False

    False. Getting good special education services in the school is very important for these children.

14. If your child has a developmental disability and needs special services, this does not need to be part of your parenting plan. True False

    False. Your parenting plan should address any special needs your child may have.

15. Finally, in your own words, tell why it is important for a mother to understand child development.

    ____

    ____

    ____

    ____

    ____

Lesson 2-2: Infancy and Toddlerhood (0-2 years)

Developmental Tasks of Infancy and Toddlerhood

Babies learn to trust other people during infancy. Infants are totally dependent on others to meet their needs. Babies must have trustworthy caretakers to learn trust. If caretakers do not soothe, feed, and change the baby regularly, the child may have difficulty trusting people in the future.

A caretaker (usually the mother, but it could be the father) tends to the infant's needs more than 2,000 times in the first year of life. It does not matter to babies who soothes, feeds, and changes them, but someone must. These contacts build the child's sense of trust. It also helps them bond with people. Being able to make these early attachments is very important for all future relationships. Even a very young infant comes to know the primary caregiver's voice and face. Changes are confusing to infants, and you should avoid them as much as possible.

During the second year of life (the start of toddlerhood), children learn to walk. Walking is a very important change for children. Walking allows children to explore and manipulate the world. The main task of toddlerhood is to become more independent. Toddlers begin to recognize that they are separate from the person or persons who care for them. However, they need close supervision because they have little knowledge of dangers.

Physical and Motor Development

The first year of life is one of rapid growth. The average birth weight is 6.5 to 9 pounds. Do you remember how much your first baby weighed and how long he or she was? Fill in the blank with your best guess. ______lbs. _____inches. Newborns lose about 6 percent of their birth weight within a few days, but gain 5 to 6 ounces per week during the first month. Babies with low birth weights may have more physical problems.

At first, most babies' movements are automatic behaviors that help protect them. These include things such as swallowing, sucking, gagging, coughing, and blinking. Newborns sleep seventeen to nineteen hours a day, although they may wake up every few hours. Newborns have fairly good hearing, a sense of smell, and the ability to visually follow moving objects if they move slowly enough.

By four to eight months, their teeth begin to appear, and most children have more than doubled their birth weight. By this time, they can use their finger and thumb to pick up objects. They can move objects from one hand to another. They can hold things such as their bottle. Most children can roll over by this time. Never leave infants alone on a bed, sofa, or changing table. They could easily roll off.

Between twelve and twenty-four months, most children can crawl, stand alone, rise to their feet without support, and walk without help. Babies develop motor skills to move around. Other motor skills such as crawling, creeping, and walking are important for mental development. Such activities help eye-hand coordination and promote mental growth. Recent research discourages the constant use of walkers, as young children need the freedom of being on the floor to allow them to develop large motor skills. Healthy motor development leads to better reading skills.

By the second year of life, infants can help feed themselves. They enjoy holding utensils and drinking from a cup. Expect frequent spills. Infants this age are able to stack objects, turn pages in a book, and play hiding games. At age two, most children gain some control over using a potty. Toilet training, however, is usually not completed until around age three or four. Boys tend to be later than girls. Be patient; do not rush it. Many cultures allow children to learn this at their own speed. They respect the natural order of development.

Some parents find small rewards (cereal or bits of candy or cookie) helpful when the child is able to use the toilet appropriately. However, never scold or punish when the child has an accident. It is best to just clean the child up and put the child on the potty for a few minutes every hour or so. Reading children a book when they are on the potty may help them relax and think of the potty as interesting and fun.

Mental and Language Development

Listening to people talk is very important for babies in their early years. This is how the baby learns to speak. Infants let others know what they need through crying. With practice, parents can tell what different cries mean. Loud noises startle infants. Generally, they like sounds such as music and human voices, especially the voice of the person who takes care of them. By twelve months, most children know their own name. Young children understand different tones of voice. Loud, angry voices frighten them.

Talking develops rapidly around twenty-four months. Before that, children may understand many words, but they usually cannot talk easily. By the time the child reaches twenty-four months, you should understand about half of your child's speech. Most children can follow simple directions and use simple sentences. By this time, they may know five to fifty different words. The words they learn first usually have to do with animals, food, and toys. At this age, children enjoy rhymes and songs. Naming things is an important activity. It helps build language. Although toys are fun and useful, children learn most through the attention of and play with the caregiver.

Social and Emotional Development

Each child is unique. Newborns are very different from each other. Newborns' most important task is to form a close relationship with the person who cares for them.

By four months of age, infants react to different voices. They will frown when voices are loud, angry, or strange. Even at this age, infants enjoy routines such as bathing and getting their diapers changed. They will smile at friendly faces and make sounds.

At about eight months, children think of themselves as separate people. They often feel uncomfortable around strangers. They are able to laugh aloud. They also become very good at copying other people's expressions and sounds. They can tell the difference between strangers and family members.

Around the age of one year, many children have a fear of strangers and of being alone. Children want the parent to be in constant sight. Children may ask to be picked up by sticking out their arms. They may become very attached to toys and certain objects such as their favorite blanket. They quickly can recognize their own name. They also jabber a great deal. They may repeat any behavior that gets them attention.

As toddlers get older, they become less cuddly. They become demanding and easily frustrated. Part of this is just becoming independent. They may get upset when you try to stop them from running, climbing, or touching things. Toddlers also cannot share and are very possessive. "No" and "mine" are favorite words. They may spend a lot of time protecting their toys from other children. Children of this age can play alone for a short time. They enjoy being held and like someone to read to them. They can recognize themselves in a mirror and are curious about other people and about their surroundings. They get into everything and require close supervision at all times.

By age two, children show signs of caring for others. They still will hit other children when frustrated or angry. Temper tantrums often hit their peak during this time. You cannot reason with a child throwing a tantrum.

Two-year-olds are impatient and cannot wait to take turns. They enjoy helping with household chores. They copy other children's behavior. Making choices can be very difficult since they want it both ways. They are often defiant. Shouting "no" becomes automatic. They want routines to be exactly the same all the time. They can be very bossy. A few children may develop the habit of biting when they are frustrated. Take this seriously. The first time it happens, firmly tell the child, "No." Also, watch closely to make sure the child is not experiencing too much frustration. The mother may need to get help from a counselor or day care professional on ways to deal with her toddler.

Discipline Methods for this Stage

No physical discipline is required for infants. Never spank or shake an infant. Spanking infants is cruel and unnecessary. It may seriously hurt the child. Shaking is especially dangerous. It can result in serious brain damage or death. If your baby gets too difficult to manage and you are frustrated and upset, take a break. Quickly, get someone to help you. You should plan for this in your parenting plan (which you will develop at the end of this course).

Babies need lots of contact from people. You cannot spoil babies by holding them too much. It is important at this stage to childproof your house. Childproofing is making your house safe from dangerous objects (sharp objects, cleaning supplies, poisons, electrical cords, choking hazards, and other dangers). If your child wants something that is dangerous, distract her and provide a safe object (toy, book, or other object) instead. Once the child begins creeping, you must keep the floors clean and free from all clutter, as everything will go into the child's mouth. Being a responsible parent not only involves the actual care of the child, but it also means providing a safe, clean environment.

You will manage your infant more easily if you develop daily routines. These routines include regular waking-up, feeding, dressing, napping, bathing, and going-to-bed times.

Discipline for toddlers mostly involves making the environment safe and setting up routines. Make sure the child does not get overly tired or hungry. This can go a long way to keep the child from getting cranky.

Mothers always should remove children from dangerous situations—even if the children fuss and do not like it. You can distract a toddler with a safe toy and redirect the child by tickling or beginning some other play. Ignoring bad words or behaviors and not giving attention by making a fuss often decreases unwanted behavior. Some early childhood experts believe that having a large dog in the house with a young child is dangerous. Children should never be left alone in a room with a dog.

Rewarding desirable behaviors with praise is also appropriate for this stage. Children this age can only learn so much, however. Sharing, for example, is very difficult for most toddlers. Often, if they give a toy away, they expect it to be given right back. They may think that sharing is the same as giving something away.

Use natural or logical consequences (explained in more detail in a later lesson) for older toddlers, so long as the consequences are not harmful or dangerous. For example, if the child makes a mess, he can help clean up.

Voices and Viewpoints

Christina says, "Our baby is six months old. I think she's spoiled. She cries all the time. She will not stay in her crib alone. We can never get any sleep. My husband says she needs a spanking, but I'm not so sure. He's getting fed up and so am I. We shouldn't have to put up with this."

What do you think? Can a six-month-old baby be spoiled? What could you do in this situation?

____

____

____

____

____

____

____

____

____

____

Experts never recommend spanking. Yet, toddlers respond well to touch. Touching them softly on the arm, picking them up, taking them by the hand, holding them, or gently hugging them are good ways to get their attention.

Finally, it is important to set a good example since toddlers copy their parents. If you hit a child, he may copy this behavior with other children. Set good examples of those behaviors you want your child to learn. Some times you have to control your own angry behavior before you react to your child.

Important Things to Remember about the Toddler Stage

Enjoy your baby, but do not expect her to understand everything. Soothing, comforting, and holding infants does not spoil them. Children at this age have little control over their feelings or behaviors. Keep them in a safe environment. Divert and redirect their unwanted activities. Establish routines. Praise and reward desired behaviors. These are the most effective approaches. It is also important to set limits and not allow destructive, aggressive, or dangerous behaviors. You may pick children up and hold them to stop such things. However, never use spanking, shaking, and other forms of harsh punishment.

Exercise 2-2: Infancy and Toddlerhood

Directions: Read each question carefully and write in your best answer.

1. Why do you think it is impossible to spoil an infant?

    ____

    ____

    ____

    ____

2. Do you think it is possible to teach a toddler to share?

    ____

    ____

    ____

    ____

3. Why do you think spanking and shaking an infant is never a good thing to do?

    ____

    ____

    ____

    ____

4. What sort of discipline methods are best to use with young infants?

5. What sort of discipline methods are best to use with toddlers?

6. Why is it important to set a good example for toddlers?

7. How can you control your anger before you discipline your child?

8. What is the most important thing that an infant needs to learn?

____

____

____

____

9. What is the most important thing a toddler needs to learn?

____

____

____

____

10. Why are learning to crawl and walk so important to the child?

____

____

____

____

11. If you wanted to teach your toddler to be kind and gentle with pets, how would you do this? Why is this important?

____

____

____

____

Lesson 2-3: Early Childhood (3-6 years)

Developmental Tasks of Early Childhood

The major developmental tasks children learn in early childhood include:

1. Improving coordination and movement skills such as climbing, skipping, pouring, using scissors, writing, drawing, and so forth
3. Completing toilet training
4. Developing more self-control of behaviors and feelings
5. Begining to understand the idea of right and wrong

Physical and Motor Development

By age three, children improve their movement skills. They can scribble, handle a fork and spoon, use zippers and buttons, and help feed and dress themselves. Washing and drying their own hands and brushing their teeth help them feel good about themselves. Children of this age may become frustrated when something is difficult. They need a lot of praise and encouragement. Parents need a lot of patience to teach young children self-control. Parents are children's first teachers. Children will copy their parents, even parents who do not control their anger and frustration.

From ages three to four, children usually have good muscular control. By the end of this time, they usually are toilet trained. Often, they can feed and dress themselves. Most can peddle a tricycle by this time. Most have all of their baby teeth.

From four to six years, children can handle rounded scissors and pencils safely. They especially enjoy musical activities. Their activity is very high, including a lot of running and climbing. By six years of age, most children are also able to hop, skip, and jump. During this time, children become right-handed or left-handed. Do not try to force them to change hands.

Mental and Language Development

From ages three to four, the child's memory and attention span improves. Most can work on a task for up to fifteen minutes. Children can sort and name objects, and they show an interest in the world around them. At this age, children have a lot of active fantasy play. They may focus all of their attention on play. They may love to make up stories. They also begin to understand how things happen. They can understand how one thing causes another to happen. Be ready for lots of questions.

Children at this age experiment with swear words. As this will be a problem when they enter school, it is best to calmly discourage the use of swear words. However, you may not be able to do this if there is a great deal of swearing at home. Most children at this stage love to hear the same stories over and over again. Most of them can speak in sentences of up to five words by this time.

From age four to six, they like make-believe play. Children of this age are quite good at sorting objects such as blocks, toys, and colors. At this time, they begin to understand simple math concepts. By the end of this time, children are able to understand simple rules and play group games. They can follow directions. Children at this age also begin to see humor and love to laugh. Pretending, telling wild stories, and engaging in fantasy thinking is still quite strong, and you should not view it as a problem at this age. By the age of six, they are usually able to speak well and are interested in learning new words. The number of words they can use usually doubles from age three to six.

Social and Emotional Development

Three-year-olds want to please their parents. They may copy their parents' behavior. They are very sensitive and aware of comments that adults make. Three-year-olds enjoy being around other children. Although they understand the idea, sharing is still difficult because of their self-centered nature. They may shove and hit when they play with other children. Some children suddenly become more strong-willed and disagreeable than before. They also show signs of insecurity and aggressive behavior. This occurs because the children are moving toward more independence. They may get new fears. The most common fears are loud noises, animals, taking a bath, and the dark. Listen carefully and comfort your children when they are afraid. Never tease children about their fears.

As they get a little older (ages four to six), they begin to feel guilt and understand when they have been naughty. Most children have feelings of guilt and shame for the first time in this stage. Children at this age may be moody. Many children brag and make up tall tales. Children may experiment with lying and stealing. You can handle these behaviors by calmly talking to your child. Reading books to them on the subject can also be helpful. At this stage, it is normal to have an imaginary playmate.

By age six, children are more self-confident. Nightmares and bedtime fears are still common. Using nightlights, leaving the door open, decorating the bedroom, and providing rewards for sleeping in the room, all can help with these problems. However, constant night terrors (when the child is very upset and cries violently) probably should be discussed with the child's doctor or a counselor. Children of this age are able to be away from their parents for longer times. They also are better able to control their behavior and participate in give-and-take relationships. Children at this age still seek the approval of their parents.

Voices and Viewpoints

Kayla says, "Britney, my four-year-old daughter, stole a candy bar from the grocery store. She put it underneath her shirt. When I asked her where she got it, she lied to me. I think she needs a good spanking."

Jasmine says "I do not think four-year-olds know about stealing. I think you should tell her she was wrong and make her give back the candy bar. She has to learn to say she is sorry."

What do you think should be done? Do you have any other ideas about how to deal with this problem?

____

____

____

____

____

Discipline Methods for this Stage

Discipline methods for the stage of development often involve giving or withholding attention. For minor misbehaviors, not giving attention can be very effective. Some parents walk a few steps away and just ignore a child who is throwing a tantrum. Most children will get up and try to follow a parent who walks away. Try to focus attention and praise on desirable behaviors. Often, if you divert the children's attention to something more interesting or redirect their behavior by hugging them or handing them something fun, you can prevent tantrums.

Rewarding good behavior with praise and attention is the most effective discipline method at this stage. Children at this age will work very hard for parental attention and approval. You may use timeouts effectively to temporarily remove children from situations in which their behavior is out of control. Timeouts remove attention and give the child time to regain some internal control. The chapter on positive discipline explains timeouts in more detail.

Never use yelling, name-calling, or spanking. They do not work and just cause more problems.

Important Things to Remember about This Stage

Perhaps the most important thing to remember is to enjoy this stage of development. Early childhood is a time when children are developing very quickly. They are becoming more and more their own persons. Children of this age are quite affectionate. They are more likely to get colds and other illnesses due to increased contact with other children. Make sure they get medical checkups and immunizations. Because of the danger from accidents, safety issues are very important in this stage. Lesson 4-2 offers more details on safety issues.

Finally, make sure you take time to interact with your child. Do not overuse television or videos to baby-sit your child. Establish good communication routines at this early age. What your child wants more than anything is you.

Exercise 2-3: Early Childhood

Directions: Read each question carefully and fill in your best answer.

1. List at least three important things that a child must learn in the early childhood stage.

 ____

 ____

 ____

 ____

2. If your child had a nightmare, how would you go about comforting him or her?

 ____

 ____

 ____

 ____

3. What are some of the discipline methods that work best with children during early childhood?

___

___

___

___

4. During early childhood, if your child makes up stories that are not true, what should you do?

___

___

___

___

5. Why should you limit the amount of time your child spends watching television?

___

___

___

___

6. Most children complete their toilet training during early childhood. If your child still has accidents, what are some things you might want to try?

___

___

___

___

7. Why is it important to listen, talk to, and read to your child during early childhood? How does this help him or her?

8. In general, how do children in early childhood feel about their parents?

9. List four fun activities that you could do with four-to-six-year-old children?

10. List at least three chores that a four-to-six-year-old child could help with at home.

Illustration by Michael Kotz, *Body of Thought Too*

Lesson 2-4: Childhood (7 to 11 years)

Developmental Tasks of Childhood

This stage takes place during the elementary school years. The main developmental tasks for this stage include the following:

1. Adjusting to school
2. Developing feelings that they can do things for themselves
3. Learning how to work with others
5. Acquiring basic school skills (reading, writing, arithmetic)

Physical and Motor Development

From ages six to nine, physical growth is somewhat slower. Children of this age may appear a little overweight until they grow taller. Coordination increases at this age. Many can play in group-sports activities such as baseball, soccer, or volleyball.

Girls may experience a growth spurt starting around age ten. Some girls may begin puberty around ten or eleven years of age, although it is quite normal for it to begin a few years later. Puberty is the time when the body produces chemicals called *hormones*. Hormones cause bodily changes. These include: growth of body hair, voice and skin changes, the beginning of girls' periods, and the development of sexual characteristics. By the end of puberty, the body is capable of sexual reproduction. Boys' sexual development is usually a few years later (starting at twelve or so). By age eleven or twelve, permanent teeth replace baby teeth. Even at this time, bone growth is still incomplete.

Mental and Language Development

Around age seven or eight, children's thinking suddenly becomes more mature. They are able to understand ideas that are more difficult. At this stage, they begin using logic to make decisions. They are better able to think through things. Since memory improves, they also have a greater storehouse of information on which to base decisions. They have a greater understanding of right and wrong. Better language skills lead to better self-control. Like most adults, children at this stage often talk to themselves as a way to guide their behavior. They advance in reading, writing, and math skills.

Social and Emotional Development

At the beginning of this stage (seven to nine years), some children are quite moody. They may be demanding and uncooperative. As they learn more, they also are afraid of more things. They need a lot of assurance that they are safe. Gradually, they learn more self-control and develop the ability to consider other people's feelings. This is an important time to work with your children in developing their problem-solving skills.

During this stage, children usually make best friends. Often, they talk more with friends than family members. Signs of emotional trouble in this stage include bedwetting, headaches, and other physical complaints. Constant sexual play (to the point of physical irritation) and frequent sexual themes in drawings and play may indicate possible sexual abuse. Most children will not tell adults that they are being sexually abused.

In the last part of this stage (ten to eleven years), children increase their curiosity about the opposite sex. Talk to your child about bodily changes and sexual issues at this time. Be honest and simple. Depending on the child's maturity, discuss possible risks such as pregnancy and sexually transmitted diseases.

Children at this time can be very sensitive about their appearance. Be cautious about name-calling or making comments about how the child looks. Girls in particular are prone to eating disorders. If a child is overweight, your help might include planning a healthy diet, limiting treats, and seeing that your child gets more physical activity or exercise. However, do not put too much emphasis on weight. Do not hound children about what they eat.

Fitting in with their friends is the priority at this stage. Friends may pressure them to take part in sexual behavior or substance abuse. Talk to your child about these issues. Let them know where you stand. But, do not constantly nag. At this time, children tend to be very honest and often show a strong personal and social conscience.

Discipline Methods for this Stage

In the early part of this stage, timeout and redirection to another activity still may be effective. While rewarding desirable behavior still works, parents' approval is no longer a strong reward. This is because approval by friends is so powerful. Money, desired objects, and privileges are generally more effective rewards with older children. Make sure you choose the reward that is most important to your child. This is often an individual matter that may require several tries before you pick the best reward.

Voices and Viewpoints

Carlotta says, "If I tell my son Juan he can't do something, he always says, 'all the other kids are doing it.' I tell him, 'I do not care what the other kids are doing. You're not doing it.' Then, he gets mad and says that I'm not fair."

What do you think? Is Carlotta unfair? What did your parents say to you when you said, "All the other kids are doing it"? What would you say?

____

____

____

____

____

____

____

____

____

Using natural and logical consequences (letting them experience the effects of their mistakes) can be helpful if the behaviors are not too dangerous. Because they are older and can understand things better, they can lean from these methods at this stage. Of course, a parent must allow her child to face whatever consequence or punishment results from this child's choice. Children will not learn to make better decisions if their parents always bail them out.

Parents use sanctions, such as grounding and taking away privileges, most often to discipline children in this age group. While these can work well, they can often be more effective when combined with rewards. Developing a behavior contract with both rewards and penalties can be very helpful.

Important Things to Remember about This Stage

School, peers, and the coming of puberty are the major issues at this stage. School plays a big role in how your child feels about himself or herself. Success in school is related to higher education and jobs in the future. Lesson 5-2 will discuss the things mothers can do to help encourage good school achievement. Taking an interest in the child's schoolwork and speaking positively about school sets the stage for good grades.

Relationships with friends are extremely powerful in influencing your child's behavior. As much as possible, you need to help your child find a desirable group of friends. Getting into trouble is much more likely if your child spends time with friends who have behavior problems. If you have ever been in a gang, think about how it affected you. Do you want your child to have the same fate? Let your children know about their choices.

Finally, the coming of puberty sets the stage for adolescence—the last stage before adulthood. Communication, as always, is very important, as is the child's need for good information.

Exercise 2-4: Childhood

Directions: Carefully read each question and write in your best answer.

1. Why does parental approval lose its power in late childhood? Whose approval becomes most important to the child?

   ____

   ____

   ____

   ____

2. If you do not take an interest in your child's schoolwork or if you are constantly saying bad things about the school, what will that do to your child's school performance?

   ____

   ____

   ____

   ____

3. Why is it important that your child spend time with friends who are good citizens and role models?

____

____

____

____

4. What are some of the good things and bad things about using restrictions (such as grounding them) as a discipline method?

____

____

____

____

5. Why is it important that you discuss things such as pregnancy and sexually transmitted diseases with your child?

____

____

____

____

6. Think back to when you were in junior high or middle school. What were some of the things that you worried about then?

____

____

____

____

7. Do you think preteen children should have jobs around the house? What sort of chores would be best for them?

8. Which one of these three things would you be most concerned about and why? (1) The way your child decorates his room, (2) the way your child dresses, or (3) if your child starts smoking.

9. What are some signs of stress in preteen children?

10. Girls tend to develop faster than boys. How do you think girls feel about this? How do you think boys feel about this?

Illustration by Fred Mumford, *The Herd and Feed Bin*

Lesson 2-5: Adolescence (12+ years)

Developmental Tasks of Adolescence

Adolescence is the last stop before adulthood. Preparing for this is challenging and scary. Both children and mothers struggle as the child becomes independent. Here are some of the major developmental tasks of adolescence:

1. Establish a comfortable identity, liking who you are
2. Develop a capacity to have close personal relationships (love and sex)
3. Prepare for future jobs
4. Become independent from parents

Physical and Motor Development

During adolescence, children attain adult sexual maturity. Puberty takes about two to four years. Girls are usually one to two years ahead of boys in reaching puberty. Gradually, the boys catch up. Puberty starts with internal chemical changes. These changes can affect moods. Both boys and girls can be very moody during adolescence.

Most girls in the United States begin having their periods between the ages of twelve and thirteen years. Both boys and girls have a major growth spurt during adolescence. Physical growth is complete for girls at about sixteen years and for boys at about seventeen years. It is not unusual for boys to add more than ten inches in height and more than forty pounds in weight during adolescence. Growth can be very rapid. Some adolescents grow four inches and gain twenty pounds a year.

Throughout puberty, girls have an increase in fat deposits, which lead to feminine curves. Boys' fat deposits decrease, and they add muscle mass. Pimples may develop in early adolescence, especially in boys. This may be a serious problem for some youths due to the bad effects on their self-image. A doctor can help with complexion problems. Girls may feel both proud and self-conscious about their physical development during adolescence. Make sure you talk to your teenagers about the changes they are experiencing and what they can expect. Tell them about your own struggles. Try to be sensitive to their feelings. Go ahead and buy the training bra, even if there is no need for it.

Generally, adolescents are relatively healthy. Yet, even at this age, your main job is to help your children protect themselves and to live healthy lives. Auto accidents are the leading cause of death among adolescents, followed by homicides and suicides.

Seventy-three percent of adolescent boys and only 57 percent of girls report regular exercise. You can encourage your children to participate on school sports teams. As a rule, adolescents do not get enough sleep. Just as in the child's earliest days, setting routines for eating and regular bedtimes will help them to be alert to the challenges they will face. School, work schedules, and activities take up most of the time.

Mental and Language Development

People used to believe that adolescents think the same way as adults. This is not the case. The brain continues to change throughout the adolescent years. Gradually, adolescents develop more logical thinking and problem-solving techniques.

Adolescents often show immature thinking patterns. Their immature thinking causes many problems. These patterns are also frustrating and difficult for parents to understand. The most common immature thinking patterns are the following:

- **Idealism:** Thinking that the world should always be fair and perfect. This leads to a lot of complaining about fairness.
- **Criticalness:** Thinking that nothing is ever good enough. This leads to much criticism of virtually everything and everyone.
- **Argumentativeness:** Being irritable and unwilling to cooperate. This leads to many fights with parents and other authorities.
- **Indecisiveness:** Being unable to make decisions and paralyzed by fears. This leads to a lot of dawdling and time wasting.
- **Self-Consciousness:** Being overly sensitive, especially regarding "looks." This leads to being very worried about what other people think.
- **Beliefs about Being Special:** Believing that people should treat you better because you are special. This leads to demanding special privileges.
- **Beliefs of Invulnerability**: Believing that nothing can harm you. This leads to doing foolish and dangerous things.

Be aware of these thinking patterns. They often cause many of the conflicts between parents and adolescent children.

Adolescents have a large vocabulary and enjoy word games. They are interested in the latest slang. They often create their own language. This personal language sets them apart from others. They feel special, and it fosters feelings of independence.

Adolescents have a keen sense of justice. They often fight because they think things are unfair. Some of this comes from immature thinking, but some is from a genuine sense of justice. As their thinking matures, they base their judgments on internal principles rather than just the fear of being punished.

Social and Emotional Development

Some have labeled adolescence a time of storm and stress. Much of this tension comes from outside pressures. Adolescents must make many adjustments on the road to adulthood. One of their major tasks is to come to terms with their parents. Adolescents have very mixed feelings about their parents. On one hand, they love them and are dependent on them. On the other hand, they are trying to break away and become independent individuals. Most adolescents do not rebel openly against their parents. In fact, most adolescents hold the same basic values as their parents. Generally, parent-child conflicts are centered on everyday things such as:

- Drinking, smoking, and using substances (alcohol and drugs)
- Going out at night and using the family car
- School, grades, and homework
- Completing chores
- Money
- Dating and sex

Having people they can talk to and do things with is very important for girls during adolescence. Knowing who they are and standing up for themselves is often more important for boys.

Developing a sexual identity often puts adolescents in conflict with their parents. Sexual experimenting, masturbating, and even occasional same-sex experiences are common during adolescence. Some adolescents are unsure about their sexuality. Later in adolescence, some may firmly decide that they prefer same-sex relationships. Mothers may not be happy to hear what their older children tell them, but they must be accepting and supportive to keep the lines of communication open. What is most important is trying to prevent risky and dangerous behaviors.

Adolescents who are overly sensitive about their appearance often start following self-destructive diets or taking drugs to improve their appearance. Eating disorders, unfortunately, have become common in adolescent girls. Look for possible signs of eating disorders such as drastic weight loss, stopped menstrual periods, refusal to eat at all, self-induced vomiting, or too much exercising. If you see these symptoms, get professional help.

Risk for drug abuse increases as children enter early adolescence. Marijuana, alcohol, and tobacco are still the most popular drugs with adolescents. Talk to your child about this issue and be alert for any signs of substance abuse. Rebellious and destructive behavior can become a problem during this stage, especially if friends are frequently getting into trouble. Besides their friends, the amount of supervision you provide and how you discipline are the main factors in determining whether your child will get in trouble with the law.

Encourge your teens to do well in school even if they are having problems. Convince them of the importance of completing at least high school and not dropping out of school when the going gets tough.

Discipline Methods for this Stage

Effective discipline for adolescents requires a cooperative effort between the adolescent and parents. Parents cannot enforce many of the things they could in the past. It is important that parents set "enforceable" limits. It may be difficult or impossible to make the adolescent behave in certain ways. However, you can plan what you will do as a mother. By focusing on your own controllable behavior, you can help reduce some of the powerlessness you otherwise may feel in dealing with adolescents. Some of the things you can control are the following: recreation privileges, access to the car, money, your own behavior, and other resources.

Rewarding desirable behavior is still a powerful tool, but the adolescent is the one who has to decide what effective rewards are. Often, approval from friends is such a powerful reward that it may be stronger than anything that parents can offer. Natural and logical consequences, where the children directly see and have to experience the result of their own behavior, can be an effective discipline tool. We will discuss this in detail in the next chapter.

Behavior contracting is a very powerful discipline tool, developed particularly for adolescents. It involves working together and respects the child's growing independence. Typically, a good behavior contract sets up clear expectations for behavior and rewards and penalties. The contract provides rewards for desirable behavior and penalties for unwanted behaviors. Grounding and restricting and removing privileges are usually effective penalties. A good behavior contract takes away some of the direct conflict between parent and adolescent. The adolescents know ahead of time what will happen when they commit certain acts. Thus, they cannot blame the consequences on the parents' being "unfair." Contracts help minimize the unfairness issue.

Of course, discipline during adolescence is much easier if you have established good communication in the past. The best foundation is a loving relationship from the child's earlier years. Some of the things that parents can do to improve communication with teenagers include:

- Give your undivided attention when you talk to your teenager.
- Listen calmly, and concentrate on hearing and understanding their thoughts and feelings before you speak. Take ten deep breaths, if necessary.
- Speak to your teenager in the same courteous tone you would use with a stranger.
- Begin by repeating back to your teenager what you heard her say, without approval or disapproval in your voice ("So you feel . . . You think . . . I hear you saying . . .").
- Recognize immature thinking patterns, and do not take them personally.
- Keep the door open for any subject (especially sex). Try to be approachable.
- Avoid humiliating your teenagers. Never name call or laugh at their comments or questions, and never tease them about sensitive areas.
- Encourage your teenagers to participate in legal activities of their own choice.
- Praise and thank your teenagers frequently.
- Let your teenagers take part in family decisions, but avoid placing worry about bills, your relationships, or other adult problems on their shoulders.
- Understand that your teenagers will need to challenge and reject some of your beliefs to grow up and become their own person.

Important Things to Remember about This Stage

Achieving personal, sexual, social, and a job identity is very hard. Adolescents today are under a lot of pressure. Fortunately, they have many strengths. They have tremendous energy and drive. Encourage them to use this energy toward completion of high school. They have a concern for the future of the country and the world. They are willing to take risks for other people and have a strong sense of fairness. Adolescents tend to be open and honest. They often have a good sense of humor. Many adolescents think very deeply and seriously about issues. As they get older, they are sensitive to other people's feelings. Try to help your child use these strengths.

Finally, remember your importance as a role model. You may be pleasantly surprised when you find out your children's values are the ones you wanted them to have.

Voices and Viewpoints

Darlene says, "My fifteen-year-old son, Cody, went to juvenile court the other day. The judge threw the book at him. Sure, they caught him riding in a stolen car, but he wasn't the driver. I think two years at the state juvenile correctional facility is too much punishment for a first-time offense. I don't know why they can't give him a break."

What do you think? Was the judge too harsh? If you were Cody's mother, what would you tell him?

____

____

____

____

____

____

____

Exercise 2-5: Adolescence

Directions: Read each item carefully and fill in your best answer.

1. Think back to when you were sixteen years old. At that age, what things were important to you? What do you think about those things now?

   ____

   ____

   ____

   ____

2. What immature adolescent thinking pattern annoys you the most and why? If you do not have a teenager, think back to your own time as an adolescent.

___

___

___

3. How do adolescents feel about their parents?

___

___

___

4. What are some of the advantages and disadvantages in using grounding as a discipline method with adolescents?

___

___

___

5. What are some of the strengths that adolescents have?

___

___

___

6. What are two ways you can improve communication with a teenager?

___

___

___

7. Give two reasons why it is a good idea to use behavior contracts with adolescents.

___

___

___

8. What are the main developmental tasks of adolescence? What do you think is hardest and why?

___

___

___

9. If your son or daughter tells you he or she is dropping out of school, how can you convince him or her not to do so?

___

___

___

10. If you cannot control your teenagers' behavior, what are some other things you can control that might help?

___

___

___

11. When you were a teenager, what things did you and your parents argue about?

___

___

___

Chapter 3

Using Positive Discipline with Your Children

This chapter deals with one of a mother's most important responsibilities—providing positive discipline. In four lessons, you will learn how to set limits and use positive discipline. You will learn how to be consistent and how to choose effective rewards and penalties. This chapter will explain methods that are effective for younger children and approaches that are useful for all ages. We also discuss natural and logical consequences as effective techniques to help children learn from their experiences.

Finally, this chapter discusses punishment and the effective use of sanctions (penalties) as a disciplinary method. We present current thinking about punishment for you to consider.

The positive discipline method you use should always fit with the child's developmental level. Some methods may work well at one stage, but not at others. The chart on page 80 shows the positive discipline methods and the developmental stages at which they are most effective.

Discipline Methods at Different Developmental Stages

Discipline Methods	Developmental Stages			
Stage / Years	Infancy (0-3 yrs)	Early Childhood (4-6 yrs)	Childhood (7-11 yrs)	Adolescence (12+ yrs)
1. Planned Ignoring of a Problem Behavior	Good	Good	Good/Fair	Fair/Poor
2. Diverting Attention to Something Better	Good	Good	Good/Fair	Poor
3. Redirecting Behavior to a Better Choice	Good	Good	Good/Fair	Poor
4. Timeout	Ineffective	Good	Good	Poor
5. Reinforcing Behavior	Good	Good	Good	Good
6. Use of Sanctions (grounding, loss of privileges)	Ineffective	Poor/Fair	Fair/Good	Good
7 Behavioral Contract or Agreements	Ineffective	Ineffective	Ineffective	Good
8. Natural Consequences of Their Choices	Ineffective	Poor/Fair	Fair/Good	Good
9. Logical Consequences (you mess it up, you clean it up)	Ineffective	Poor/fair	Fair/Good	Good
10. *Physical Punishment*	Not Recommended	Not Recommended	Not Recommended	Not Recommended

Lesson 3-1: Positive Discipline for Younger Children

What Is Discipline?

One of your most important jobs as a mother is to teach your children how to obey the rules. You can do this by using positive discipline with your children. Discipline is not the same thing as simple punishment. Physical or other harsh punishment leads to bad feelings such as anger and fear. Punishment may temporarily stop an unwanted behavior, but at a very high cost. Harsh punishment teaches very little and has unwanted emotional side effects that may remain with your children their entire lives.

Positive discipline means training your children so that they will behave in a way that you think is right and stay out of trouble. Positive discipline methods encourage good feelings instead of anger and fear. The goal of positive discipline is for the child to develop self-control. Teaching your child self-control is a difficult but rewarding task.

The Right Attitude

Often times, mothers become very angry when children misbehave. Sometimes this anger can lead to harsh and ineffective punishment. Discipline is not getting even for bad behavior. Discipline is not just the expression of anger. Children should clearly see that their mother disapproves of certain bad behaviors. The right attitude for positive discipline is one of loving instruction—not anger.

Many incarcerated mothers who rejoin their families feel guilty that they have been gone. Many try to make up for being absent. They think they can make up by not disciplining their children or setting any limits. They believe this is being good to the children. While the children may like this, this is *not* being good. Providing the right kind of positive discipline is always the best thing a responsible mother can do for her children. Some mothers who feel guilty may buy many expensive gifts for their children. They may foolishly spend much-needed family money on toys and recreation. A responsible mother knows that her attention is the best gift. There is no need to spend the family money recklessly out of a sense of guilt.

It is important that your children see you as a competent adult who is in control and will work on taking care of problems. You want your children to see you as an adult who is not perfect, but who takes responsibility for her actions. You also want them to see you as a person who admits to mistakes, will listen, but sticks to the rules.

Voices and Viewpoints

Jasmine's four-year-old daughter, Shanice, has started biting other children in her preschool class. She began doing this when her sister was born. When Jasmine hears about this, she feels very angry. She is embarrassed. She also is worried that Shanice will get kicked out of school. That night, Jasmine screams at Shanice and spanks her very hard. She says she will get a spanking every night until she stops biting.

Maria also has a four-year-old daughter, Angel, who started biting children in her class, when her brother was born. Maria thinks it is funny and laughs when Angel tells her about it. She decides that Angel is just showing some spirit. She thinks Angel will outgrow it. She does nothing about it.

Do you think that Jasmine used positive discipline? Give your reasons.

____

____

____

____

____

____

Do you think that Maria used positive discipline? Give your reasons.

____

____

____

____

____

____

Do not let yourself be begged or argued into bailing out your children or forgetting the consequences for misbehaviors.

Positive Discipline Methods Primarily Used with Younger Children

Very young children have a hard time understanding things. They are unable to pay attention and have poor self-control. Because of this, some discipline methods are not very useful. In this chapter, we will examine four positive discipline methods that are very useful with younger children. These methods are the following:

- Planned Ignoring
- Diverting Attention
- Redirecting Behavior
- Taking a Timeout

These methods do not work as well for older children and adolescents.

Planned Ignoring

Planned ignoring is a very simple positive discipline method. It is based on the idea that many unwanted behaviors take place because they lead to increased attention. Attention from parents (especially mom) is a very strong reward for most young children. Behavior that is rewarded tends to increase. Ignoring takes away the reward of attention. In many cases, ignoring the behavior is all that is required to get rid of an unwanted behavior.

Steps in Using Planned Ignoring Effectively

1. Identify a problem behavior that seems intended to get your attention. It must be one that is not dangerous.
2. Plan to withhold your attention by ignoring the behavior.
3. Do not say anything. Do not make any facial expression. Avoid eye contact.
4. As soon as the child is doing something more desirable, quickly give your attention. Praise the new behavior.
5. If after repeatedly withholding attention, the behavior does not decrease, switch to another method.

Voices and Viewpoints

Two-year-old Andrei has just learned to say the word "poo poo." Most people think this is very cute and laugh when he says it. Andrei says it all the time. Andrei's mother, Jolene, notices that Andrei says the word over and over at home, trying to get a rise out of her. Jolene has planned to ignore it. She looks away when Andrei starts saying the word. She only gives Andrei attention when he picks up a toy or a book. After a while, Andrei gives up and starts playing with his toys.

Why do you think Andrei quit saying the word "poo poo"? Do you think you could ignore this behavior? If not, why not?

____

____

____

Diverting Attention

You may use this positive disciplinary method with younger children. The method involves switching the child's attention from an activity that is likely to lead to trouble to something else. Diverting means switching from one thing to another. For example, a two-year old girl is about to take another child's toy. She might be diverted from this activity if you call her attention to a favorite storybook. This method is often used with babies. Babies may come across dangerous items while they are crawling. If the baby starts toward some dangerous object, you easily can switch his or her attention to other things that are safer.

Since babies cannot pay attention very long, you usually can divert them. Simply approach the baby in a friendly way and offer a safer object, such as a ball or stuffed animal. If the baby cries, try some other safe object. If the child does not do what you want, physically assist her. For example, gently pick up the child and turn her around to face the safe object. You may need to repeat these steps several times.

Diverting attention is an easy way to avoid meaningless struggles with children who are too young to understand rules. Diverting attention requires that the mother be very alert to possible problems so she can head them off before they grow into big ones.

As children try out different behaviors, they may learn some unwanted ones. Children keep doing them because they get their parents' attention. We call these *attention-seeking behaviors*. Parents give them attention to try to get the child to stop. Do not get caught in this loop. Even negative attention (scolding, nagging, or yelling) may be rewarding at times. Ignoring these attention-seeking behaviors while giving attention to more desirable behaviors is a very effective discipline method. No discipline method, however, works 100 percent of the time. You may have to try several methods to find the one that works best for you and your children.

Steps in Using Diverting Attention Effectively

1. Be alert and identify an upcoming problem. (You see two-year old Helene heading toward her older brother's CD player.)
2. You identify some things that would divert her attention (for example, a snack, reading a familiar book, playing with a favorite toy, or some activity she enjoys such as being tickled).
3. Offer the child the most reasonable alternative ("Helene, do you want to go with Mommy and have a cookie?").
4. If the first alternative does not work, try one of the others. ("Helene, let's read about Dora the Explorer®" or "Helene, let's play with your Mr. Mouse.") You may have to assist her physically to look at the object.
5. If the method still does not work, switch to redirecting the behavior. (Pick Helene up and take her over to the couch and read to her.)

Redirecting Behavior

This technique is similar to diverting attention. It involves guiding the child physically to perform some more desirable behavior. Redirection is also called "assisted compliance" since you are helping the child obey a rule. For example, a child who is about to hit another child with a toy might be redirected by a parent by removing the potential weapon and asking the child to draw a picture. When using this method, you often have to move the child physically. This might involve lifting the child up and moving her. Sometimes you take some object away. It is important that you do this firmly, but gently. Do not grab or scare the child.

For children who are older, you first can ask them to do something else. For example, if your son is throwing a ball inside the house, you can set up some paper cups and ask that he try bowling instead. You have redirected him to rolling the ball instead of throwing it. You could tell a child who is tossing blocks around, "I see you are having a hard time playing with your blocks. Let's find something else to play with now. When you remember the rules, you can play with the blocks again."

Use redirection in dangerous situations, if you are careful. Again, you begin by giving a direction. At the same time, you immediately help the child obey the direction. For example, say your daughter starts to ride her tricycle into the street. First, you would firmly tell her to "stop!" and at the same time, you take hold of the tricycle to stop it. When she is not in danger, you can explain that she could get hurt by riding in the street.

Steps in Using Effective Redirection

1. Remind the child of the rule, "You do not jump on the bed."
2. Give a choice, "You may sit on the bed or you may jump on the floor."

Note: Never just keep repeating yourself, without getting up out of your chair to back up your instruction. Failing to take direct action is lazy parenting. It teaches children that parents are helpless to correct them and that they do not have to listen.

3. If the child does not do as requested, physically assist her to do so. For example, gently take the child from the bed and place her on the floor. You may need to repeat these steps several times before the child cooperates.

Timeout

This method involves removing the child from the current situation for a short time. During the timeout, it is important that the child does not get any attention. The best places for timeouts are hallways, the parents' bedroom, or some corner or chair where there is nothing to distract the child. The child's bedroom is usually not a good place. There are too many interesting things there. Never use a bathroom, cupboard, basement, closet, dark room, or area that might frighten the child. The purpose of a timeout is to stop the child from getting attention for unwanted behavior. Timeouts should never last more than one minute for each year of the child's age and never exceed more than five minutes altogether. A kitchen timer is ideal to use for a timeout. When the timer rings, the timeout is over.

During timeout, the mother must *not* give any attention. This means do not speak, scold, or explain. Remember, even negative attention can be a reward. Timeouts will not work if you give any rewards. Some children will refuse to go to the timeout area. When this happens, you must gently, but firmly, lead the child to the timeout area. Do this without anger or comment. If you use a corner and your child tries to leave before the timeout is over, immediately return her to the corner. Stand close by, but avoid eye contact.

You should not use timeouts for infants and younger toddlers. Timeouts are most effective for children between the ages of two and six years. Very young children should not be totally isolated or ignored. You should always be able to observe your child during a timeout. Infants and young toddlers who do not understand why their behavior is wrong should be redirected to other activities. Do not use timeouts too often. If you do, they will no longer work. A timeout should be a last resort.

Steps in Using Effective Timeouts

1. Tell the child the rule to be followed.
2. If your child does not obey within five seconds, say, "If you do not follow the rule, you will have to take a timeout." Some parents count to three.
3. If your child still does not obey within five seconds, say, "Because you did not follow the rule, you have to take a timeout."
4. Lead your child to the timeout area without explaining, scolding, or arguing (this is very important).
5. Ignore shouting, crying, or promises to obey. Avoid eye contact.
6. Tell your child to sit in the timeout chair or stand still in the corner facing the wall. When your child is quiet, set the kitchen timer (one minute for every year of age, up to a maximum of five minutes).
7. When the timer rings, say, "Timeout is over." Repeat the rule. Let your child know that now he has a fresh start and can make a better choice. Use a timeout again if your child still does not obey. Stop after using it four times in a day, and consider some other technique.
8. When your child obeys, praise her so she learns what behavior is expected.

Exercise 3-1: Positive Discipline Methods for Younger Children

Directions: Read each paragraph carefully and answer the questions which follow.

1. **Planned ignoring**: Tameika and her mother, Chandra, are in a constant battle over slamming the car door. Chandra picks up Tameika every day, and on the ride home, she talks with her about her day at preschool. Tameika does not like preschool very much. Often, these talks end with Tameika slamming the car door. Today, Chandra says nothing and decides to give attention to another behavior. She says, "Tameika, thanks for helping your little brother with his backpack today. You were a good sister."

What behavior is Chandra ignoring?

____

____

____

What behavior is Chandra giving attention to instead?

____

____

____

What problem needs to be addressed?

____

____

____

2. **Planned Ignoring**: Corina has put three-year-old Martina to bed. Martina has gotten a drink, a hug, and her favorite stuffed animal. Corina has turned on the nightlight. When Corina turns off the ceiling light to leave the room, Martina begins crying. Corina thinks, "It's time for Martina and the rest of the family to go to sleep. What should I do?" She makes sure Martina is okay and then leaves the bedroom. She ignores the crying, making sure Martina is safe by peeking through a crack in the door. The next morning, she praises Martina for being such a brave girl and staying in her bed last night. She talks with Martina about plans to make the bedroom even more special.

   What behavior is Corina ignoring?

   ____

   ____

   ____

   ____

What behavior is Corina giving attention to instead?

3. **Diverting**: Two-year-old Kayla is fascinated by the television's power switch. She is always turning the set on and off. Her mother, Ann, sees Kayla moving toward the television. She calls her name and holds up her favorite stuffed animal. Ann holds it as though she is rocking it in her arms. Kayla quickly turns away from the television and comes over to play with the toy instead.

   Do you think Kayla would have come over if Ann had held up a pillow instead of a favorite stuffed animal? Why or why not?

4. **Redirecting:** Helena sees three-year-old Luis heading toward his older sister's toys. The family calls him "Hurricane Luis" because he likes to shake her toys until they scatter. Before Luis can reach the toys, Helena runs over and scoops him up, tickles him, and shows him a new picture book.

   Why is this a better way to deal with this problem than yelling at Luis or spanking him?

5. **Timeout:** Five-year-old Nathan often grabs toys away from his three-year old brother, Terrell. Liza, his mother, has told Nathan that if he takes one of Terrell's toys again, he will have to take a timeout. Nathan grabs Terrell's Hot Wheels® car. Liza tells him he must take a timeout. Nathan refuses to go to the timeout corner.

   What does Liza have to do now to make sure this timeout works?

   ____

   ____

   ____

6. **Timeout:** Four-year-old Janice has started biting her younger sister when she refuses to do what Janice wants. Joan, the girls' mother, has told Janice that if she bites her sister, she has to take a timeout. Joan has set the timeout to be fifteen minutes long. When she tells Janice to go to time out, she screams at her and tells her she is stupid for biting.

   What mistakes did Joan make? How can Joan use timeouts better?

   ____

   ____

   ____

   ____

Lesson 3-2: Positive Reinforcement: The Key to Better Behavior

Positive Reinforcement

Positive reinforcement of good behavior is probably the most important child-discipline method you will learn. It is the most powerful tool available to change behavior. Positive reinforcement is another way of using rewards. Positive reinforcement means consistently rewarding the child for desirable behavior. In other words, when the child does something that you want to see increase in the future, you reward it. The reward can be an object such as a toy or food. It also can be praise, affection, or attention. For older children, it can be a privilege such as watching TV or going to the movies. The reward must be something that the child values and for which he will work. We will discuss picking the best rewards later in this lesson. Below is how positive reinforcement usually works.

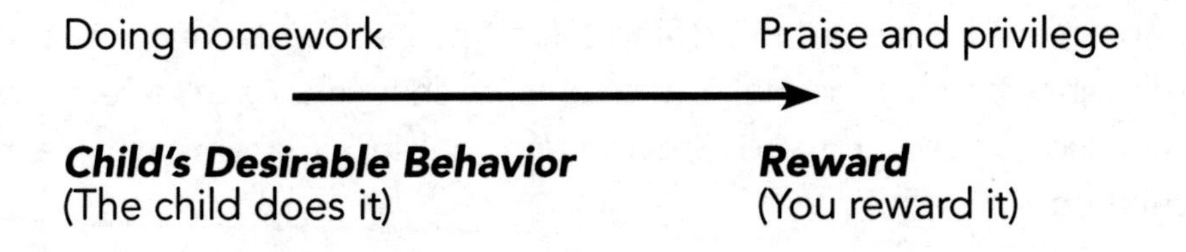

Rewards are much more effective than punishment. They tell children what they are supposed to do. Punishment only tells the child what not to do. Some mothers do not like to use rewards. They say it is bribery. Rewarding good behavior is not bribery. Bribery occurs when you reward someone for dishonest or bad behavior. You bribe someone not to do his or her job. For example, people may try to bribe a policeman so he will not do his job (not give them a ticket). You pay people to do their jobs. People receive rewards for doing good jobs. Give the reward after the job is done; it is never given for just the promise of doing the job

All about Rewards

There are many different types of rewards. We call some of the best *social rewards.* Social rewards are things such as praise, attention, affection, and approval. Social rewards come from other people. Because most children value their mother's approval, they usually will work hard to get it. No matter what type of reward you pick, add in the social reward of praise.

Of course, no children have to earn their mother's love. You should give affection unconditionally. This means that you show your love whether your child has had a good or bad day. Children should not have to earn things such as meals, birthdays, and trips to see grandma. Thinking your children are terrific and having a strong, positive relationship with them is the most important thing that you can do to help your children ultimately succeed in life. Social rewards such as praise can help you teach your children the behaviors and life skills they will need.

Use several types of rewards with your children. Social rewards are always good; however, children may become tired of other rewards if you use them too often. You can use small toys, stickers, pictures to color, puzzles, games, and other fun items as rewards. Keeping rewards small is best. Mothers use foods as rewards, especially for younger children. It is best to use healthy foods and limit the use of candy or junk foods with high sugar content. Whenever you use an object or food as a reward, also use praise and attention. The connection between the object and the praise helps strengthen the reward value of the praise. The best situation is one in which the child wants your approval and works hard to get it.

You can use special privileges and activities as rewards. This includes such things as going to a movie, going out for ice cream, doing a craft project, or having a friend spend the night. Allowing the child to make decisions, such as choosing a restaurant or picking out clothing, also can be a reward. Staying up a half-hour later may be a special reward for some children.

Psychologists have discovered that you can use any activity that children do repeatedly on their own as a reward. This can be helpful in finding rewards for children who do not seem to like the usual rewards. For example, if a child stays in his room and just sits on his bed a great deal, you can use the privilege of going to your room and sitting on your bed as a reward. You can use this privilege to reward other behaviors such as doing chores or completing homework. So, one way to discover effective rewards is to watch carefully what the child does when she is left to her own choices. You can use any acceptable activity that occurs a lot as a reward.

How do you know if a reward is effective? This answer is easy. Positive reinforcement is a very practical method. An effective reward is one that works. If children will work for the reward, and they change their behavior, then the reward is effective. If no change occurs, then you need to select another reward.

Steps in Using Effective Positive Reinforcement (Rewards)

1. Choose the behavior you wish to increase (always pick the smallest one that you think will work). If you have more than one child, select a behavior to work on for each child so that no one is singled out.
2. Count how often this behavior takes place now (this is called "getting a baseline").
3. Choose a reward that you think will be effective for your child (you could discuss this with your child).
4. Begin giving the reward whenever the child performs the desirable behavior. Remember to use praise along with whatever reward is selected. You could put a chart on the refrigerator to record your child's progress.
5. At first, give the reward every time the behavior occurs. Later, when the new behavior is firmly planted, lessen the reward and only give it occasionally to keep the behavior going.
6. If the behavior has increased from the baseline level, you know the positive reinforcement has worked. You could give weekly bonuses for increases in the positive behavior.
7. If the behavior has not increased from the baseline level, chances are you did not pick a good enough reward, or you did not give the reward consistently enough. You may have picked too big a behavior to learn all at once. Go back to step 1. Make sure the behavior is something your child can do, pick a better reward, and try again. Also, see if you can break the behavior into smaller steps. Start rewarding the first step. (For example, if your goal is get two brothers to get along better, you first might reward the act of just walking away from arguments without hitting. Later, you might reward actually helping the person.)

Sample Chart to Monitor Behaviors

Tommy's Chart for Picking Up His Toys

	Sun	Mon	Tues	Wed	Thur	Fri	Sat
Week one	☺	☺		☺		☺	
Week two	☺		☺	☺	☺		☺
Week three	☺	☺	☺	☺	☺	☺	☺

Voices and Viewpoints

Heather says, "I like this positive reinforcement stuff. My kids seem to learn better, and I feel like I'm teaching them something."

Delores says, "I do not like the idea of rewarding my kids every time they do something good. They should just be good naturally. This is like bribing them to be good."

What do you think? Should kids just be good naturally? Do you think positive reinforcement is the same as bribing? Why or why not?

____

____

____

____

____

Decreasing a Behavior: Rewarding Incompatibles

Often times, your goal is to stop or decrease a problem behavior. The problem behavior could be fighting, dawdling, making a mess, talking back, goofing off, riding a tricycle in the street, or a hundred other things. You still can use positive reinforcement to reduce how often these behaviors take place. To do this, you can use a method called *reinforcement of incompatible behaviors*. An incompatible behavior is some behavior that is the opposite of the problem behavior you are trying to decrease. For example, you cannot fight and cooperate at the same time. If you reward cooperation, the amount of fighting will decrease naturally. You cannot ride a tricycle on the sidewalk and ride it in the street at the same time. Therefore, if you reward riding on the sidewalk, riding in the street will decrease.

So, if you wish to reduce a problem behavior, the first step is to figure out a desired behavior that is incompatible with the problem behavior. Then, follow the steps for positive reinforcement of the desired behavior. The list on the next page gives several examples of incompatible behaviors.

Problem Behavior	Incompatible Behavior
Being late	Being on time
Fighting	Cooperating
Making a mess	Cleaning up
Talking back	Acting respectfully

Now, write down some behaviors that are incompatible with these problems:

Problem Behavior	Incompatible Behavior
Eating junk food	________________
Ignoring homework	________________
Goofing off	________________
Watching too much television	________________

Point Systems

Some mothers find point systems are very helpful. In a point system, the child receives points or some type of marker (such as a poker chip) as a reward for certain desirable behaviors. The behaviors are usually things such as doing chores, getting along with brothers and sisters, completing homework, or cooperating. The mother sets up a system so that each time the child performs these behaviors, he or she gets a certain number of points. The mother sets the times for the child to cash in these points. Usually the mother has some type of reward menu with things and activities listed along with the number of points required to earn them. Some rewards may be large and require many points to earn (such as a bicycle); others may be small treats (such as a favorite food for supper). Point systems operate like a checking account or a commissary system. You must have credit in your account to purchase things. Mothers sometimes use point systems in homes when there are several children who are close in age to each other. Because you can have so many different types of rewards, point systems are often very effective.

Behavior Contracts

Use behavior contracts with older children, especially adolescents. The parent and child work together to develop a list of duties and privileges. If the child successfully performs the duties listed, you can then award the privileges as stated in the contract.

Having this written agreement can help reduce conflicts in the future. Sometimes behavior contracts have bonuses for extra, fast, or excellent performance. Behavior contracts may also have sanctions. These are penalties for failure to perform. Sanctions usually involve losing some type of privilege. Below is an example of a simple behavior contract.

Sample Behavior Contract

Ashley and her mother agree to the following terms:

Duties:

1. Ashley agrees to have her homework completed by 8:30 p.m. on nights when there is school the next day.
2. Ashley agrees to be in the house on weekends by 10:30 p.m. unless she makes special arrangements in advance with her mother.
3. Ashley agrees that she will not take any calls on her cell phone after 10:00 p.m. on Sunday though Thursday and 11:00 p.m. on Friday and Saturday nights.

Privileges:

1. If Ashley has her homework done by 8:30 p.m. on school nights, she will not have to take the bus to school the next school day; she will be dropped off at school.
2. If Ashley is in the house by 10:30 p.m. on weekends, she will be allowed to visit her best friend the next Monday.
3. If Ashley is on the cell phone after the times set, she will loose possession of her phone for two days for each infraction.

We both agree to this contract:

Child	Date	Parent	Date
Ashley Jones	10/10/08	*Brenda Jones*	10/10/08
Ashley Jones		Brenda Jones	

Problems Using Positive Reinforcement

Behavior Is Too Big to Learn All at Once: Sometimes the behavior we want to increase is too large or complicated to learn all at once. If this is the case, the best thing is to break the behavior into smaller steps. You can reward the first step until the child completely learns it. Then, you can add the next step. Do this until the child learns all the steps. This method is called *chaining.* Each piece is like a link in a chain. You can use chaining to teach children complicated tasks such as reciting a poem or dressing themselves. You can break the poem down into stanzas and reward the memorization of each stanza separately. Eventually, the child will have learned all the stanzas. Then, he can link all the steps together and recite the whole poem. Teaching children to dress themselves is similar. You can start out teaching them to put on their shoes and socks, and then teach them how to put on and button a shirt. Finally, you teach them how to put on pants and a belt. Reward each step until it is completely learned.

Behavior Does Not Take Place Often Enough to Reward: Some mothers might complain, "How can I reward him for cooperating with his sister if he never does it?" If this is the case, it is helpful to explain and show the behaviors you would like to see. Then, ask the child to demonstrate the behavior for you. The child may need to do this several times. Later, when opportunities to show cooperation occur, you can remind him of the behavior you are looking for. This reminder is called a *prompt.* You can remove the prompt once the behavior becomes more frequent. Some parents hang up posters listing the rules for behavior. This is a good way to prompt desirable behavior.

The Reward Does Not Seem to Work: This is one of the most common problems. Fortunately, the solution is fairly easy. Just switch rewards. Often times, mothers think something will be a good reward, but the child does not see the reward as valuable. You can do very little to increase the value of a reward. It is simpler and quicker to just switch to another one. Ask your child for help in selecting a reward.

Failing to Be Consistent: This is a very common problem. Sometimes parents do not consistently reward the desirable behavior. Sometimes they forget. Sometimes they are not organized enough. Other times, parents may get angry at the child and revert to negative discipline methods. For positive reinforcement to work, you must give the rewards consistently and without criticism or anger.

Exercise 3-2: Using Positive Reinforcement

Directions: Read each paragraph carefully and answer the questions below.

1. Seven-year-old Timmy has been wetting the bed. The doctor says there is nothing physically wrong with him. It seems that he just does not get up from bed and go to the bathroom at night. Timmy has wanted to save up to buy a certain popular action figure. Timmy's mother, Bonita, tells Timmy that she will put a quarter on the back of the toilet tank each night. If Timmy gets up and uses the bathroom, he can take the quarter. Even if he does not get up to use the toilet, if his bed is dry in the morning, then he also can take the quarter.

   What two things are being rewarded?

   ____

   ____

   Why do you think a quarter is a good reward for Timmy?

   ____

   ____

2. Pamela constantly comes home late for supper. Her mother, Crystal, started rewarding her with praise for getting home on time. If the reward is effective, Pamela will develop the habit of arriving on time for supper.

   What is the problem behavior?

   ____

   What is the incompatible behavior?

   ____

   What is the reward?

   ____

3. Eight-year-old Fernando is constantly leaving his mother's scissors lying around the house. His mother, Raquel, tells Fernando that if she comes home from work and the scissors are in the drawer, she will read to him for fifteen minutes from his favorite storybook.

   What is the problem behavior?

   ____

   What is the incompatible behavior?

   ____

   What is the reward?

   ____

4. Sadie decided to reward ten-year-old Jarrell for getting better grades in school. She told Jarrell that he would get $5 for each "A" he received on his nine-week report card. For the first two weeks, Jarrell seemed to be doing his homework and trying harder in school. But soon, he was back to his old habits of not doing his homework and not studying for quizzes. When the nine-week report cards came out, Jarrell received no "As."

   Why do you think this method did not work very well?

   ____

   ____

   ____

   ____

   What could Sadie do to improve her approach?

   ____

   ____

   ____

   ____

5. Toni is trying to teach six-year-old Brianna better manners at the table. Brianna often eats with her fingers and makes a mess. She knows how to use a fork and spoon but just does not like to do it. Toni tells Brianna that if she remembers to use the fork and spoon for the entire meal, she will play a game of checkers with her. On the first, night Brianna did well and did not eat with her fingers. She was eager to play checkers. Toni had intended to play with her, but her favorite program was on television. She told Brianna that she would do it later. Soon, it was too late to play and Brianna had to go to bed. The next night Brianna did not do so well, she used her fingers and did not get a reward.

   What big mistake did Toni make the first night?

   ____

   ____

   ____

   ____

Lesson 3-3: Natural and Logical Consequences

In this chapter, we examine two positive discipline methods that teach children the effects of their own behavior. Children can learn that their behavior has good and bad results that directly affect them. We call these results *consequences*. Children often think that mothers do not have good reasons for making rules. They believe they are just being bossed around. Using natural and logical consequences helps teach the child that rules have a reason.

Natural Consequences

Although the use of natural consequences is a positive discipline method, it has an aspect of mild punishment. In natural consequences, you allow children to experience the direct effects of their unwanted behavior. For example, if a child leaves her possessions lying around the house, the mother would put the things in a box and not give them back for a few days. It is just like in the real world, where if you leave valuable things lying out, they usually are not there when you return. In another example, a girl does not put her dress in the laundry basket, so she cannot wear her favorite dress to school the next Monday because it is dirty. Natural consequences require some thinking and imagination to be effective.

Natural consequences are the things that would happen naturally if you did not pick up the slack as a parent. Natural consequences can be great teachers. Natural consequences let the child learn personally, the hard way, without entering into conflict with the parent. So far as possible, children should experience only *safe* risks. They can learn a great deal from this school of "hard knocks." The main reason children do not learn from natural consequences is that many parents often overprotect them. Although we hate to see our kids upset or disappointed, it is better if parents do not shield their children from all natural consequences. ***However, you always must intervene to protect your child from harm or injury.*** You must never use natural consequences if the child might be injured or permanently harmed.

Working with natural consequences usually means allowing events to run their course. However, if the consequence is too far in the future, you will want to find a substitute logical consequence. For example, failing to do schoolwork can affect one's long-term opportunities. You do not want to use the natural consequence of "not being able to get a decent job" in the future. This would be far too destructive. Instead, you can set a logical consequence such as, "If you are too tired to do your homework, then you are too tired to play video games and must go to bed." Or, "If you are too sick to go to school, then you are too sick to get out of bed."

In natural consequences, the real world provides the lesson. When natural consequences are used, no lecture is necessary. Never use natural consequences if the child is in danger of hurting himself or others or is destroying property. Some cultures use natural consequences quite extensively, and occasionally outsiders think these parents are being neglectful because they do not intervene very much. They are not being neglectful; it is just that these cultures have a great respect for the natural order of things and nature's role as a teacher.

Logical Consequences

Logical consequences are quite similar to natural consequences and overlap at times. Logical consequences occur when you make the child pay a price for committing an unwanted behavior. The price must be logically connected to the unwanted behavior. For example, a child who makes a mess on the floor is made to clean it up. A child who writes on the wall is required to wash it. Use logical consequences when natural consequences are not available or suitable. Connect the logical consequence directly to the behavior you wish to change. Logical consequences must make sense to the child. The child should easily see the connection between his or her behavior and the outcome.

Undoing is a form of logical consequence. In this method, you direct the child to undo or correct something that he did wrong. Fixing things, cleaning up messes, paying for things, or writing personal apologies are examples of undoing. Writing an essay to show you understand what you did was wrong is another good example. In the case of the child who writes on the wall, if you make the child wash only the writing off the wall, this would be undoing. If, however, you had the child wash the entire wall, not just the part that he wrote on, that is an example of another method, called *overcorrection*.

Another example of overcorrection is that a child who tracks dirt into the living room is made to vacuum the entire house. In overcorrection, the child not only has to undo his past poor behavior, he must make things better or he must rehearse the desired behavior until it is perfect. Another example of overcorrection would occur when a child who runs in the house must walk slowly through the house several times until his parents are satisfied. Use overcorrection very carefully so that it does not become cruel or abusive. It can be a very useful method of discipline.

Tips on the Use of Natural and Logical Consequences

Apply consequences immediately after the unwanted behavior. Parents should tell the child in advance what the consequences are for breaking rules. If children know the

Voices and Viewpoints

Sarah says, "The only way kids learn that the stove is hot is if you let them touch it. I taught my kids to swim by throwing them into the water."

Vickie says, "I think kids need to know the consequences of their behavior. If they do something stupid, they have to live with it. But I do not think putting kids in danger is the way to teach anything."

What do you think? Is Sarah correct? Or, can you teach children that the stove is hot in other ways? What do you think about what Vickie says? Is it ever right to put your kids in danger to teach them a lesson?

____

____

____

____

____

consequences, they have a choice. Children can learn to understand that they have choices and learn to accept the consequences of their choices.

Do not use empty threats. At best, threats just teach a child to be afraid. They do not produce desirable behavior. If you make threats that you cannot carry out, your children will learn that they do not have to listen to you because you do not mean what you say. Define rules clearly. Set consequences ahead of time so that the child knows what the expectations are. This reduces the "unfairness" complaint.

Do not let negative consequences build up. Children need to experience the negative consequences as quickly as possible to connect it to the behavior. They also need to get the negative part over so they can move ahead toward behavior that is more positive. Do not give up after a few tries. To have a lasting effect on behavior, you need to repeat consequences often over time. Whenever a child gets away with an undesirable behavior with no consequence, this rewards the bad behavior and makes it even harder to change.

Effective discipline often means using several methods at once. You may want to use logical or natural consequences to reduce some problem behavior. At the same time, you can use rewards to teach opposite behavior. For example, the child who tracks mud into the house may have to clean the floor. You also should reward him for removing his shoes before entering the house.

Exercise 3-3: Exploring the Uses of Consequences

Directions: Read each paragraph very carefully and answer the questions below.

1. **Natural Consequences**: Five-year-old Andrew wants to play outside. When his mother, Linda, asks him to wear his jacket, Andrew tells her that he does not need it. Instead of making him wear it, Linda lets him make his own choice. A few minutes later, Andrew comes back in the house to get his jacket. Instead of saying, "I told you so," Linda says, "Good idea, Andrew. It is cold outside."

   If Linda had simply forced Andrew to wear the jacket, what would Andrew have learned? How would Andrew have felt about his mother? When would you not want to use this method?

   ____

   ____

   ____

   ____

2. **Logical Consequences**: Six-year-old Rita rode her new bike into the street right after her mother told her to ride only on the sidewalk. Her mother, Sheila, set a logical consequence for this behavior. Shelia took away Rita's bike for the rest of the morning.

   What will Rita think about the next time she gets her bike out to ride?

   ____

   ____

   ____

   ____

3. **Undoing**: Jasmine's mother told her eight-year-old daughter not to kick her soccer ball in the backyard. She kicked the ball anyway, and it broke a window. Jasmine has $25 saved up for a new soccer ball.

   What do you think Jasmine's mother should do?

   ____

   ____

   ____

   ____

4. **Overcorrection**: Nine-year-old Destiny is always slamming the front door. Once she even put a crack in the door window.

   Using logical consequences, what are some ways that Destiny's mother could teach her to close the door gently instead of slamming it?

   ____

   ____

   ____

   ____

5. Your five-year-old child tries to run ahead of you in a crowded mall.

   Is it best to use natural consequences in this situation? Why?

   ____

   ____

   ____

   ____

6. Your child leaves a toy outside after you repeatedly told her to bring it in.

   Can you use natural consequences in this situation? Why?

   ____

   ____

   ____

   ____

7. Sixteen-year-old Ron won't get out of bed to get to his summer job.

   Is it best to use natural consequences in this situation? Why?

   ____

   ____

   ____

   ____

8. Your preschool child wants to play with knives, matches, or things in the medicine cabinet.

   Is it best to use natural consequences in this situation? Why?

   ____

   ____

   ____

   ____

9. Your six-year old daughter is threatening to hit another child with a hammer.

   Is it best to use natural consequences in this situation? Why?

   ____

   ____

   ____

   ____

10. Your eight-year-old daughter does not water the flowers she planted.

    Is it best to use natural consequences in this situation? Why?

    ____

    ____

    ____

    ____

Lesson 3-4: Punishment and Sanctions

What is Punishment?

Most incarcerated mothers are experts in punishment. They know that punishment is when you have to pay a penalty for some act. Punishment is a negative discipline technique. Most experts do not recommend the use of punishment as the primary discipline method for children, and there are two main reasons for this:

1. Punishment is not very effective in changing behavior. In most cases, it only temporarily stops a behavior. Punishment does not tell you what you should be doing instead. It provides the child very little information.

2. Punishment brings with it all kinds of bad feelings, including shame, anger, guilt, and resentment. Oftentimes, negative feelings get attached to the mother instead of being connected with the behavior that led to the punishment.

The Punishment Model

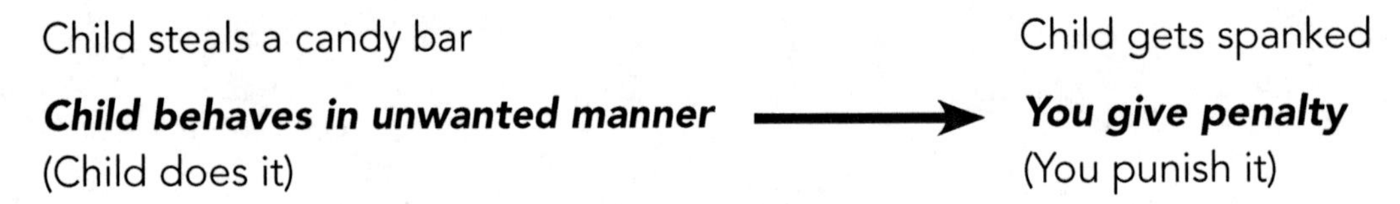

In punishment, an unwanted behavior is followed by some type of unpleasant outcome. These unpleasant outcomes are penalties. These penalties fall into one of three groups:

1. ***Physical or corporal punishment:*** This includes spanking, swatting, hitting, shaking, slapping, or otherwise inflicting physical harm or pain on the child.

2. ***Emotional punishment:*** This type of punishment involves saying things that attack the child's esteem and create bad feelings. Name calling, put downs, and yelling are examples of this type of punishment.

3. ***Sanctions:*** Sanctions are nonphysical forms of penalties that include things such as grounding, restricting, or withholding privileges. Making the child do additional work may be used as a sanction as well. Sanctions are unpleasant, but they do not have permanent harmful effects.

Note: Of these three kinds of penalties, we recommend only sanctions for occasional use. Physical punishment is not very effective; it is usually too harsh. It usually does more damage than good. Emotional punishment attacks the child's self-esteem and sense of security. You should never use it. Sanctions do not cause physical pain or damage, and they are not intended to inflict emotional harm.

Sanctions

Sanctions are penalties that do not have permanent harmful effects. Sanctions are set so that unwanted behavior costs the child something important. The cost is losing some possession, activity, or privilege. Examples of common sanctions are losing television privileges, giving up a toy, writing an essay on why you should tell the truth, and doing extra household chores. Sanctions work best when they are directly related to the unwanted behavior. These types of sanctions are the same as logical consequences. Grounding (making a child stay at home) and withholding privileges are the sanctions parents use the most. In the last lesson, we saw how you can spell out rewards and sanctions in a written agreement called a *behavioral contract.*

Voices and Viewpoints

Connie says, "I say you have to spank kids. They won't listen any other way. That's a mother's job to make the children listen."

Althea says, "I think a mother's job is to teach her kids the things they need to be successful. If you can do that without hitting them, that's great. My mom hit me all the time and all I learned was to hate her."

What do you think? Is Connie right, or is Althea? Do you have to hit kids to teach them something?

____

____

____

____

____

Guidelines for the Effective Use of Sanctions

To be effective, you must use sanctions in certain ways. The following guidelines offer some tips:

1. Give the sanction as soon as the unwanted behavior takes place. The child does not connect the problem behavior with sanctions that you give later.
2. You must give sanctions consistently. If a rule is made that certain privileges are lost if a child shows an unwanted behavior, this rule must be followed every time. If you feel sorry for the child or allow the child to talk you out of the penalty, then this method will not work.
3. Give sanctions in a routine manner. Avoid angry statements or other signs that you are upset. Sometimes getting mother upset can be a powerful reward for bad behavior.
4. Do not overdo sanctions. Do not use them for every small problem. Save them for big ones. Also, do not let sanctions build up. If a child is grounded for long periods of time, the sanction starts to lose its power. Do not use the same sanction all the time. Mix them up a little.
5. Always try to use a positive method along with the sanction. Look carefully for some desirable behavior you can praise and reward. Catch your children being good. Show that you believe that your child can be successful. Tomorrow is a new day, a fresh opportunity.

What about Spanking as a Penalty?

Throughout this chapter, we recommended not using spanking or other physical punishments. Instead, we focus on learning positive discipline methods. About two-thirds of American parents spank their children at some point. Below are some of the main reasons why parents spank children:

1. Because we were spanked as children
2. Because we do not have a better way to handle the problem
3. Because it seems to work
4. Because we are angry and want to hurt someone
5. Because the Bible tells us to do it (Spare the rod, spoil the child)

As you learn positive discipline methods, spanking becomes less necessary. Other methods are far more effective. Positive methods also leave children with a much better relationship with their mother. Often, most mothers spank when they feel frustrated and angry.

Reasons Not to Spank

Why do we not recommend spanking? Below are the main reasons for not spanking your children.

1. **Spanking hurts and humiliates children:** It can damage the relationship between child and parent.
2. **Spanking sets a poor model for solving problems:** Children may copy hitting as the best way to express themselves.
3. **Spanking can easily grow into child abuse:** This is especially true for parents with anger management problems. Some estimates show that 1,000 to 2,000 children die every year from physical punishment that has gotten out of control. More than 142,000 children are seriously injured each year.
4. **Spanking creates feelings of anger and fear in children:** Long-term studies show that childhood spanking is linked to anxiety, major depression, and drug and alcohol addiction in adulthood.
5. **Spanking is not as effective as people think:** People overestimate the effectiveness of spanking because they do not remember when spanking fails.
6. **Spanking gets overused:** Most parents who spank use that method all the time. They spank first before trying other methods. Many children get daily spankings. Parents may not even realize how often they are hitting their children.
7. **What about the Bible?** People who study the Bible have different opinions about what it really says about spanking. Some people believe the Bible encourages spanking. Other people think the Bible forbids spanking young children. In any case, the belief in Biblical teachings is a highly personal matter. People must decide for themselves. Some people may have other religious beliefs that they do not base on the Bible.

In some minority communities, child discipline can be quite strict and authoritarian. It developed this way for good reasons. First, it was important for children to obey immediately due to the terrible dangers of the hostile outside world. Secondly, it was a way to "toughen up" children so that they could deal with the cruel realities of racism and discrimination. While such traditional ways are to be respected and are not considered abuse, we still do not recommend spanking as a primary discipline approach. Spanking is generally not as effective as positive discipline. It also can have many unwanted side effects.

Managing Difficult Discipline Problems

Even after you learn how to use positive discipline techniques, some problems will still be very difficult to manage. You may need to use a combination of methods to get the results you want. Break the problems down into small pieces that you can manage instead of trying to take it all on at once. For very difficult problems, you may need to talk to an expert who works with children all the time, such as a counselor, psychologist, or a clinical social worker. These people can give you some additional hints on what to do.

Exercise 3-4a: Punishment and Sanctions

Directions: Read each paragraph carefully and answer the questions below.

1. Twelve-year-old Raven gets an allowance of five dollars a week. To get her full allowance, she must complete all of her homework before 8:30 p.m. If she does not have all of her homework completed before 8:30, her mother deducts one dollar from her allowance.

   If this sanction is going to work, what must her mother check every day?

   ____

   ____

   ____

   ____

2. Fourteen-year-old Rhonda's mother grounded her for the weekend because she stayed out past 10:00 p.m. on a school night. She tells her mother, "I do not care. I was not going anywhere anyway. This doesn't matter to me."

   What should her mother do? Should she change the sanction? Should she add another sanction? Or, should she just ignore Rhonda's comments and go ahead and ground her?

   ____

   ____

   ____

   ____

3. Wilma has made a good set of rules for her three kids. She has good rewards for the desirable behaviors and effective sanctions for problem behaviors. Her kids know the rules well. In the past, Wilma has not always followed through with things. Sometimes she is forgetful. Other times, she has been a little lazy.

   What does Wilma have to be very careful about? What could mess up her method of discipline if she is not careful?

   ____

   ____

   ____

   ____

4. Since she has been reunited with her family, Kendra has used nothing but harsh spankings and screaming to discipline her two children. The kids have started to avoid her. The children tell their father that they hate Kendra. Kendra says she loves her kids, but she does not believe in giving rewards. Because of all the yelling, one of the neighbors has called the state child abuse hotline.

   What type of punishments does Kendra use? Why do Kendra's kids avoid her? What does Kendra need to do right away?

   ____

   ____

   ____

   ____

5. Sabrina is trying to teach her teenage daughter, Polly, to be responsible and to help with household chores, so Sabrina decides to use sanctions. She sets a rule that Polly must do chores all week or she will ground Polly on Friday night. The problem is that if Polly messes up on Monday or Tuesday, she gives up for the rest of the week and does not even try to do her chores. How can Sabrina change the rule so this sanction will work better?

____

____

____

____

6. What things might you do to help address a child's behavior problem that is very complicated and difficult to manage?

____

____

____

____

Exercise 3-4b: Using Positive Discipline Methods

Directions: Keeping in mind these positive discipline methods, answer each of the following questions.

1. *Planned ignoring*
2. *Diverting attention*
3. *Redirecting behavior*
4. *Using timeouts*
5. *Reinforcing behavior*
6. *Using sanctions*

1. When you were a child, what discipline methods did people use with you? How did they work?

2. Which of the discipline methods do you like best and think you could use? Why?

3. Which of the discipline methods do you feel you might have a problem using? Why?

4. What rewards can you think of that you could use with your children?

5. What are some reasonable sanctions you might be able to use with your children?

____

____

____

____

Chapter 4

Responsibilities of Motherhood

There are three lessons in this chapter that deal with some of the most important responsibilities of motherhood other than disciplining children.

The first lesson emphasizes the importance of providing for your children. A responsible mother should do everything she can to make sure that her children's needs are met. This can be a major problem for any mother leaving a penal institution. Finding and keeping good employment can be a major challenge.

The second lesson deals with how a mother can help keep her children safe. In this lesson, you will learn the basics of child safety and how to childproof your house.

In the final lesson in this chapter, we discuss the importance of healthy family relationships for children. An African proverb says that it takes a village to raise a child. This lesson explains many of the benefits the child gets from having healthy contact with an extended family.

Illustration by Debra Butler, *Uncaged Beauty*

Lesson 4-1: Being a Good Provider

The Mother's Role as a Provider

Over the last fifty years, motherhood has changed drastically. In the past, people generally thought that it was the man's responsibility to be the provider in the family. With the large increase in divorced and single-parent homes, few women can afford to stay home and not work at all, even with young children. Single moms often worry about being able to provide for their children and manage by themselves.

Voices and Viewpoints

Christie says, "I got in trouble trying to make some money out on the street so my kids could eat, so we wouldn't have to go on welfare. I really messed up, and now I am not there to help at all. I would do anything to be able to help them now."

Bernice says, "I want to help my kids too, but I am not going to work in some fast food joint like a high school kid. I have my pride."

What you think? Do you think Christie is being honest, or is she blaming her family for her behavior? What do you think about Bernice's pride? Where does your pride lead you?

____

____

____

____

____

____

____

____

Many incarcerated women often have financial problems. Old debts, fines, lawyer's bills, and restitution payments—they can add up quickly. There is also the added difficulty of finding and holding a well-paying job when you have a prison record. All of this can result in frustration and a loss in self-esteem, increasing the likelihood that a mother might abandon her family.

Some women simply have a very difficult time earning the money they need to take care of their family. Many women are afraid of shouldering this responsibility, especially when they are the sole support for their kids. However, there are things you can do, even while still incarcerated, to increase your chances of being able to care for your family.

Getting and Keeping a Job

Although it may take time away from the children, a successful work experience is important if a mother is going to be able to take responsibility for her children. It is also a major factor in whether a person returns to prison or not. Many incarcerated women have had serious problems keeping jobs even before getting a criminal record.

Barriers to Getting and Keeping a Good Job

Here are some of the most frequent barriers to getting and keeping a good job. Check the ones that you have had problems with in the past.

- ☐ No formal education (no high school diploma or GED)
- ☐ No specific vocational or work skills (no trade skills)
- ☐ No relevant work experience (no work history)
- ☐ No job-finding skills (do not know where to start)
- ☐ No opportunities (discrimination against ex-cons, harsh environment)
- ☐ Personal presentation (dress, talk, and behave like a convict)
- ☐ Poor attitude and lack of commitment (lack of a work ethic)
- ☐ No supports (no transportation, childcare, appropriate clothing, and so forth)
- ☐ Problems dealing with authority (no skills dealing with bosses)

Many of these things may be out of your control. Others, however, you can begin working on right now. Look through the list again and see if any of the items you checked are things you can begin working on soon.

Irrational Beliefs about Work

Several barriers, such as the ones listed on page 120, deal with work knowledge, skills, and experience. These are *hard factors.* Just as important in getting a job are things such as attitude, commitment, and the ability to get along with others. These are *soft factors.* Problems with the soft factors often stem from unhealthy attitudes and beliefs. Below are several common irrational beliefs relating to work.

1. I shouldn't have to work so hard; other women have it much easier.
2. Nobody should be able to boss me around or tell me what to do.
3. If I can't buy my kids everything, then I might as well not be around at all.
4. Finding a job is too hard for me.
5. I shouldn't have to change the way I dress just to get a job.
6. I shouldn't have to follow work rules; they are unfair.
7. Other women have a man supporting them, and so should I.
8. I shouldn't have to go back to school; it's too hard at my age.
9. My boss makes me so mad. I'll show him. I'll quit.
10. I should have a more important job than this.

As you can see, most of these irrational beliefs boil down to complaining about how hard and unfair things are. You learned in an earlier lesson that you can change such irrational thoughts. The first step is to argue against the thought. You tell yourself "*No, I am not falling into that trap again!*" Then, you give the reasons why the belief is false. We call this *disagreeing with the thought.* The second step is to change the thought into one that is more helpful in dealing with the problem.

Remember the two basic steps in changing an irrational thought:

1. **Disagree:** Refuse to go down old roads that have hurt you in the past.
2. **Change:** Change the thought so that it makes sense and is more helpful to the new, stronger you.

Below are examples of how to change some irrational work beliefs using this two-step process.

Irrational Belief: *I should not have to work so hard; other women have a man to support them and have it much easier.*

Disagree: Some women may have it easier, and others may have it harder. That has nothing to do with me. I have a challenge to face, and bellyaching about it won't make it any easier.

Change: The work I have to do is hard enough; there is no need to depress myself with a bunch of negative self-talk.

Irrational Belief: *I should not have to change the way I dress just to get a job.*

Disagree: It might be more comfortable to dress the way I want, but employers want something else. They are paying for it, and I cannot control what they want. It is best not to upset myself over it. This is not worth losing a job over.

Change: I wish I didn't have to change the way I dress for work, but I can still wear what I want on my own time. On their time, it is best to give them what they want so that I can keep the job and take care of my kids.

Irrational Belief: *I should have a more important job than this one.*

Disagree: This is not the greatest job in the world, but it is a job. Maybe I will keep looking for a better one. This job helps me provide for my kids now. With some effort, I can get more education and training or maybe even get promoted. Complaining to myself only makes me feel bad. All kinds of work have honor.

Change: I would like to have a better job, so I will work on ways to get one. I refuse to upset myself about it. I am a good person because I will step up to the plate and do what is necessary.

Whenever you begin to feel frustrated or discouraged about work, use the two-step process to help change the negative self-talk into something positive and helpful. Finding and keeping a good job will be one of your most important challenges. Determination and the ability to keep plugging away is your best chance at success. Never give up!

Your Next Steps

A healthy attitude and good people skills are critical to success. While you work on these, you can do other things right now to increase your chances of being self-sufficient. These include:

1. Get your high school diploma or General Equivalency Diploma (GED) and as much education as you can.

2. Enroll in all the vocational training you can. More skills lead to more jobs. For example, many jobs today require computer and keyboarding skills.
3. Do all you can to get into a facility work program. In federal prisons, about 20 percent of the inmates work in prison industries. These jobs require a high school diploma or GED—one more reason that education is important.
4. Enroll in any work preparation, job readiness, job club, or job hunting groups that are available.
5. Find job placement resources you can use on reentry. Ask a correctional counselor, case manager, chaplain, or other staff member about job resources available in your area.
6. Realize that you will probably have to take some jobs you do not like very much, but you will need the income to support your kids. Prepare yourself to stand up to the challenge.
7. Make getting and keeping a job your major priority and commitment. Think about it, prepare yourself, and plan for it every day.
8. Start financially supporting your children as soon as possible. If you do not immediately take custody of your children, having an income and helping with the cost of their care will show the court you care about your kids. Taking control of your life and working on improving yourself and your income sends a powerful message to your children and to the authorities who will decide on custody.

Exercise 4-1a: The Mother as a Provider

Directions: Read each of the questions carefully and write down your best answer.

1. List three reasons why it is important that you get a job and provide for your children.

____

____

____

____

2. Look over the list of barriers to getting a good job. Which ones are the most important to you? List the top three barriers that you are going to work on.

____

____

____

____

3. When you were a child, was there anything special you wanted that your mother was not able to get for you? As a child, how did you feel about it? How do you feel about it now?

____

____

____

____

4. Look over the list of irrational beliefs about work. Which of these beliefs do you think might cause the most problems for you? Explain why.

____

____

____

____

5. What steps can you begin taking right now to prepare to be a better provider for your children? List at least three things.

____

____

____

____

Exercise 4-1b: Developing Constructive Beliefs about Work

Directions: For each irrational belief below, write your disagreement (your argument against the self-talk) and revision (the changed self-talk which is more helpful).

Example: Irrational Belief: "I must be perfect in my job. If I am not perfect, I am worthless; therefore, there is no reason to even go to work."

Disagree: *I am just a human being, so I will make mistakes. Being perfect is just a foolish demand that does not help me in my job in any way. Instead, it makes me feel bad about myself. Who needs that?*

Changed: *While I do not like mistakes, there is no way I can be perfect. It would be better if I try to learn from my mistakes. I do not need to blame myself. Blaming myself does not help my kids. It only makes me feel badly. My kids are a reason to keep me going to work.*

1. **Irrational Belief:** My job is just too hard. I should not have to work so hard to make ends meet. This is awful.

Disagree: ____

____

____

____

____

Changed: ____

____

____

____

____

2. **Irrational Belief:** I cannot stand this job. I feel stupid working in this place. I have to quit even though I do not have another job.

Disagree: ____

____

____

____

____

Changed: ____

____

____

____

____

3. **Irrational Belief:** I should not have to work. I'm too smart for this. There has to be an easier way to get by.

Disagree: ____

____

____

____

____

Changed: ____

____

____

____

____

4. **Irrational Belief:** If I cannot support my kids, they are better off without me. I cannot stand facing them. I should not be in their lives.

Disagree: ____

____

____

____

____

Changed: ____

____

____

____

____

5. **Irrational Belief:** I'll dress the way I want to at work. My boss should not tell me how to run my life. They should let me do what I want.

Disagree: ____

____

____

____

____

Changed: ____

____

____

____

____

6. **Irrational Belief:** I need a man to support me. I cannot make it alone.

Disagree: ____

____

____

____

____

Changed: ____

____

____

____

____

Lesson 4-2: The Mother Tiger

The Role of the Protector

Parents have always been the protectors of the family. In the past, this meant fighting off wild animals or defending the family from attackers. Today, the main threats to life are different. The role of the protector has changed from being a defender to being a good provider and protector. Today's protector needs to understand the basics of safety and good health care. Accidents, disease, and poor health habits are the major threats to children today. Dangers from other people also still exist, but these things mainly happen when the child is away from the protection of the mother. Therefore, mothers must teach their children good safety habits that can help prevent terrible things such as abduction, sexual abuse, and assault.

Accidents and Home Safety

Accidents are the leading cause of death of children under fourteen years of age. More than five thousand children a year die from accidents. Another ninety thousand children are permanently disabled each year. Suffocation, drowning, and auto accidents are the biggest accident risks for children. You can help provide a safer environment for your children by taking the time to childproof your home. Childproofing means that you go through the house and remove all dangers. Below are some basic childproofing rules for different areas of the house.

Bedrooms and Living Areas

- Put infants to sleep on their back on a firm, flat, tight-fitting mattress in a baby crib.
- Make sure your baby crib meets current safety standards.
- Remove all soft bedding and pillow-like objects from the baby crib.
- Make sure the baby crib is secure with no loose or missing hardware, or chipping paint.
- Never place a baby crib near window blinds or curtains with a cord.
- Have smoke alarms especially in sleeping areas (check regularly and change batteries twice a year).
- Use safety gates to block stairways.

- Keep small objects, including tiny toys or larger toys with small removable parts, away from young children.

Bathrooms

- Make sure children cannot get into medicines, cleaning products, and other dangerous materials. Put such items out of reach or in locked cabinets.
- Throw away old medicines, cleaning products, and supplies.
- Always check the water temperature before putting your child in the bathtub.
- Never leave the child alone in the bathtub or near any water—not even to answer the telephone.

Kitchens

- Never leave a baby alone in a highchair.
- Always use chair safety straps.
- On the stovetop, always use back burners and turn pot handles to the back of the stove.
- Make sure sharp objects, matches, and plastic bags are out of reach.

Outdoor and Vehicle Safety

- Always use child safety seats made for your child's age and weight.
- Place your young children in the backseat of the car when you travel anywhere.
- Buckle yourself and your child in on every car ride.
- See that your children wear helmets when biking, skating, or skateboarding.
- Make sure children know the road rules if they are riding bicycles.
- Do not allow children to ride in all-terrain vehicles (ATVs).
- Teach children how to swim, and teach them basic water safety.
- Always closely supervise children around the water.
- Use Coast Guard approved life jackets when boating or participating in water sports.
- Supervise young children when they are outside, especially if the yard is not fenced.

Fire Safety

- Put up a smoke alarm, test it monthly, and change the batteries regularly.
- Teach children two different escape routes out of the house, if possible.
- Teach children where all of you will meet if you must leave the house in an emergency.
- In a fire, leave the house immediately. Stay low and crawl to avoid smoke.
- In a fire, do not open any doors that feel hot; try to find another way out.
- In case of fire, call the fire department from a phone outside your house.
- Make sure that all sources of fire, such as matches and lighters, are out of reach of your children.
- Never smoke in bed.
- Make sure the electrical system is safe. Replace frayed wires and cords that are fire hazards.
- Never use the oven to warm the house.
- If you must use space heaters, make sure they turn off automatically and have been certified as safe.

General Safety

- Avoid shock and trip hazards. Use electric plug guards and do not use extension cords where people may trip over them.
- Keep sharp objects, firearms, poisons, cleaning supplies, medicines, and vitamins out of children's reach.
- Set the water thermostat to 120°F or less to avoid scalding hazards.
- Install carbon monoxide detectors.
- Keep makeup, hairspray, and other personal products away from children.
- Keep products in original containers and carefully read labels.
- Be cautious about poisonous houseplants in the house and others hazards that children might eat, such as paint chips.
- Be alert for possible choking hazards with young children, such as small toys that fast food restaurants give away and certain food such as hot dogs.
- Keep the number for the National Poison Center Hotline by each telephone (1-800-222-1222).

- Be aware of hidden hazards such as aerosol cans, bunk beds, fireworks, lawn mowers, shopping carts, and balloons. Be alert to potential problem areas such as the trunk of a car, an old refrigerator, or a garage with hazardous chemicals. Assume that your child may take out hazardous materials when you are not around.

Internet Safety

The following information from the Metropolitan Life Insurance Company provides some helpful hints for children and teenagers using the Internet. It is important to discuss these issues with your children and teenagers.

- Keep the computer in a central location, such as the kitchen or family room, rather than in a child's bedroom. This way, everyone in the family has access to it.
- Do not use computers and online services as electronic baby-sitters.
- Set and discuss reasonable rules for using the computer.
- Become familiar with the services your child can access and how they work.
- Show interest in how your child is spending time online, and have your child explain what he or she is learning.
- Consider using a pseudonym or not listing your child's name if the service allows it.
- Never give out identifying information or personal information in a public message such as a chat or bulletin board, and be sure you are dealing with someone both you and your child know and trust before disclosing identifying information in an e-mail.
- Beware of any offers that involve meeting someone.
- Never respond to messages or bulletin board items that are suggestive, obscene, belligerent, threatening or make you feel uncomfortable. Encourage your child to inform you of any such messages and, if you or your child receive a message that is harassing, of a sexual nature, or threatening, forward a copy to your service provider and ask for their assistance.
- Should you become aware of the transmission, use, or viewing of child pornography while online, immediately report this to the National Center for Missing and Exploited Children by calling 1-800-843-5678. You also should notify your online service.

Reprinted with permission of the Metropolitan Life Insurance Company.

Health Issues: Checkups and Immunizations

To protect your children from sickness, they need regular medical and dental checkups. Select a doctor who you can use as a source of information. Ask your doctor when your children should have checkups. Some children will need more frequent checkups than others.

Immunizations are the shots or vaccines that your children need to prevent them from catching serious illnesses such as diphtheria, tetanus, measles, mumps, and rubella. Ask your doctor what immunizations your child needs. As doctors learn what works best, the list of immunizations that children need sometimes change. Make sure you know what the latest recommendations are. Follow through, and make sure your child has the recommended immunizations. When you child enters school, the school will require proof of your child's vaccinations. If your child is in Head Start, the director may be able to provide some suggestions as well.

After your children's teeth come in, call your dentist or a dental clinic to see when they need a dental checkup. Do not let infants use their bottle as a pacifier or let them fall asleep with the bottle in their mouths. Begin brushing their teeth early. Use a soft toothbrush and toothpaste recommended for infants. You should teach older children to brush and floss regularly. Your dentist can tell you what your children should do to protect their teeth.

Unless you notice some problems earlier, you should get your children's hearing tested around age three to four, and get their vision checked before age five. Again, your doctor or a school nurse can tell you where you can get this done.

Health Issues: Diet and Exercise

Another way to protect your children's health is to make sure that they have a proper diet and that they get the exercise they need. Instead of each person eating when she is hungry, try to plan for family meals. It is good to have a schedule, and it gives the family a chance to talk about what the children are doing. This is one of the best times for mothers to listen to their children. Make sure meals are relaxed. Do not try to address serious problems at mealtime.

Have a variety of healthy foods and snacks (fruits, nuts, vegetable sticks) available for your children. Meals and snacks should feature fresh fruits and vegetables, whole grains (whole wheat bread, shredded wheat, oatmeal), and lean meats, eggs, and nuts. Limit processed food (like deli meats and hot dogs) and fast food to once a week. Use these as treats or privileges, not routine meals. A piece of fruit is better for your child than juice. Juice contains more sugar.

Try to be a good role model in your eating habits. Do not let your kids see you constantly eating sweets and junk food. Junk foods include things such as snack cakes, chips, donuts, pastries, candy, and other things with high calories and little food value. Limit soft drinks and drinks with a lot of sugar. Serve milk and water instead. Remember, you are trying to teach your children healthy habits while providing them with nutritious food. Involve your kids in the menu-planning process. Insist that your children eat breakfast, since eating breakfast is related to good school performance. If your child is significantly under or overweight, consult your doctor for the best diet and follow it carefully.

In addition to following a proper diet, make sure your child gets plenty of physical activity. Limit television watching to only an hour or two a day. Encourage all types of physical activity like sports as well as noncompetitive activities such as walking the dog, exercising, swimming, dancing, and skating. Arrange physical activities with family and friends so your child can get some exercise. Actively play with your children on a regular basis. Teaching them to catch a ball or ride a bike is important to their development, and doing this provides a time for you to bond together.

Set a routine time for bedtime. This can help your children get the sleep they need for good health. Children need ten to twelve hours of sleep each night, and younger children need a nap during the day.

Personal Safety

The most important way a mother can protect her children is to keep them from being exposed to anyone who might hurt them. Limit the number of people who you do not know very well coming into your house. Be especially careful about leaving your children alone with a boyfriend, even if you feel you are in love and are sure he is safe. Often, children are harmed by someone they know and trust. All children should have some idea about how to protect themselves from dangerous adults. Below are a dozen suggestions about how to teach your children personal safety skills.

1. **Do not scare your child.** Let your child know that most people are safe. While they always should be alert, they do not have to worry all the time. It is your responsibility to take precautions.
2. **Teach your child that the areas of the body covered by a bathing suit are private.** Your children should have a basic understanding of sexual issues

appropriate for their age and developmental stage. Teach your children that they should not be touched or touch other people's private parts.

3. **Teach them that sexual abuse is a crime.** They need to know that they should always tell you about anything that happens to them, especially sexual incidents. Children also should be taught that when they tell you these things, they are not being a tattletale. Children should know that sometimes bad people might threaten to hurt them or their parents if they tell anyone about the abuse. Let your children know that you will protect them and yourself. Teach them that they do not have to worry; they can depend upon you to be there for them.
4. **Teach your children that it is okay to resist by fighting, screaming, or running away if an adult tries to hurt them, touch them wrongly, or take them away.** They need to know that it is more important to get out of a threatening situation than it is to be polite.
5. **Know your children's friends and their families.** Learn as much as you can about the people your children are spending time with, including sports coaches and youth leaders.
6. **Make sure that you or some other trusted adult is always supervising your children.** This includes church activities, sporting events, scouts, and especially overnight trips. Volunteer to be a chaperone whenever possible.
7. **Teach your children never to get into a car or go away with anyone unless you have personally approved the trip.** They should not take anyone else's word, even other adults'.
8. **Trust your instincts and teach your children to trust theirs.** If you or your child feel uncomfortable about a situation, do not disregard the feeling. Check it out. When things just do not feel right, often your instincts are correct.
9. **Do not confuse children with the idea of dangerous "strangers."** Children do not have the same understanding of "strangers" that adults do. Besides, most children are in greater danger from someone they know.
10. **Teach your children what adults they can go to in emergencies.** Teach them they can go to store cashiers or clerks, police officers, other people in uniform, or people working behind a desk.
11. **Teach your children to be open and to confide in you.** It is important that your children feel that they can talk to you and not be blamed. Open communication is the best form of prevention.
12. **As their age allows, teach your children their full name, their parents' names, address, and phone number.** As they get older, also teach them how to

use 911. For adolescents, a cell phone can be a very important safety tool. Many cell phone plans now have ways to limit usage to avoid big bills.

You can practice with your children how they would act in different situations by playing the "What if" game. For example, ask your child what he would do if a man asked him to get in the car with him to go get some candy. You can ask her what she would do if a woman approached her and said that there was an accident and she needed to take her to the hospital to see you. You could agree upon a secret password that would let your children know that it is safe to go with someone and that they have your permission. Teaching your children personal safety is one of your most important duties as a mother and protector.

A Word about Gangs

Many incarcerated women may have had gang experiences. Gang membership may even be a family tradition in some cases. The gang often takes the place of the family and provides direction for its younger members. Women may get involved in gangs for many reasons, including:

1. **Protection:** Being in a gang may be a way to protect yourself in a dangerous neighborhood.
2. **Structure:** Gangs provide rules and tell you how to live your life.
3. **Nurturing:** Many women may feel that gang members care about them.
4. **Belonging:** Being a gang member gives some women a place to belong. This is especially true for women who come from very unstable families.
5. **Economic Opportunity:** Gang activities may give some women a means to earn easy money.
6. **Excitement:** Many gang activities may seem appealing to people seeking thrills.
7. **Status:** In many neighborhoods, associating with a gang is a way to get others to look up to you.

Many gangs are extremely hostile to women and promote a culture of using and abusing them. Because gangs are usually criminal and violent, preventing gang membership is one of the things that responsible mothers need to address with their children—both girls and boys. Breaking the cycle of gang activity can be very difficult. A family that works well together and has pride and loyalty can go a long way toward reducing the appeal of gangs.

Exercise 4-2: Protecting Your Children

Directions: Read each of the following questions and write down your best answer.

1. Why do children need to get medical checkups and immunizations on a regular basis? What could happen if they do not?

   ____

   ____

   ____

   ____

2. Mothers need to protect their children from many different things. List at least three major threats children face today.

   ____

   ____

   ____

   ____

3. What three types of accidents present the greatest danger to children? What does it mean to *childproof* a house?

   ____

   ____

   ____

   ____

4. What are some junk foods that you enjoy? What healthy snacks could you serve your children as a substitute?

____

____

____

____

5. What do you think are the most important things you should teach your children about personal safety? List the top three things, and tell why they are important.

____

____

____

____

6. What are some reasons people join gangs?

____

____

____

____

7. What are some things that you could do to protect your children from gang participation?

____

____

____

____

Lesson 4-3: Family Relationships and Traditions

The Importance of Family

Research tells us that the most important thing to a child's well-being is the mother. The mother is the child's first attachment. Being able to be close to another person is important for the child's emotional health. Trusting someone gives the child a sense of stability in a scary world.

Both mothers and fathers are important to children's emotional health and development. Children need both positive male and female examples in their lives. Some child psychologists say that the most important thing that parents can do for their children is to love each other. As you know, however, this not always possible. If you have a good relationship with your child's father, work as hard as you can to keep this relationship. The next chapter provides some information on communication skills that can help.

Mothers who are separated or divorced from their child's father can still help their children benefit from having two parents. This is true even if the relationship is permanently broken. If the child's father is in the picture at all, you need to do your best to make him your ally, someone you can work with. Even if your relationship with the child's father is bitter, you still have one thing in common—wanting the best for your children. This is the common ground from which you can learn to work together. This often means setting aside grudges for your child's sake.

Failure to develop a working relationship with your child's father can lead to a variety of harmful results for your children. These include:

1. Forcing children to choose between two people they love
2. Putting children in the middle of a conflict
3. Keeping children worried and insecure
4. Setting a bad example for your children's future relationships

Maintaining a Good Relationship with Former Partners

You can do several things to maintain a good relationship with your former partners. These are some of the more important rules to remember:

1. **Stay in the present.** Avoid bringing up past issues and fights.
2. **Focus on the children.** Work together to problem-solve to help them.
3. **Do not be nosy about your former partner's personal matters**. Do not bring up dating or current relationships. Do not use the kids as spies.
4. **Do not criticize your former partner in front of your children**. Try to support your children in having a good relationship with the other parent and any stepparents because this is what is best for them.
5. **Do not use your children as go-betweens**. Do not have your child carrying messages or asking for favors from the other parent for you.
6. **Teach your children respect for their father.** Even if you have issues with their father, teach your children to show respect and courtesy for him.
7. **Try to have a friendly relationship with the new partner of your children's father.** You do not want her to feel constantly threatened by you, as she is spending time with your children and can help with arrangements. You will probably need her help at times.

What if nothing seems to work? Sometimes, despite all efforts, some couples just cannot work together. When this happens, communication may have to go through a third party. Lawyers, child advocates, and mediators sometimes do this. Such arrangements are usually very expensive and troublesome. This is not the best arrangement for raising children. To avoid this situation, do all you can to keep your relationship with your children's father(s) as positive as possible.

Dealing with Multiple Former Partners

Some women may have children with several different former partners. The basic rules described above still apply in those situations. In addition, although you will need to deal with each former partner as an individual, multiple partners will make it a much greater challenge. Since former partners can help you support your children, and since it is best for a child to have a mother and a father, it is important to stay on good terms with them. Respect for your former partners is the key. Even if you do not like them, show respect for their time, their privacy, and their position as the father of your children.

It may be difficult if one father and his family visit regularly and provide for their child and others do not. It will take a lot of skill as a mother to let such neglected children know that it is not their fault and that they are just as special and valuable as the other children.

Voices and Viewpoints

Elvira says, "My in-laws have always treated me like dirt. Since I've been arrested, it has only gotten worse. Even though they have been nice to the kids, I do not want anything to do with them."

What do you think Elvira should do about letting her kids see her in-laws? Is there any way she can try to make things better?

____

____

____

____

____

____

The Family Group: In-Laws and Outlaws

Children are emotionally healthier when they know they belong to a family group. Healthy contacts with grandparents, uncles, aunts, cousins, and other relatives give children a sense of security. Belonging to a family group helps children form their identities. Families also can provide support in times of need.

In-laws also can be a major source of conflict in marriages. Women who have been incarcerated may especially have problems with critical or judgmental in-laws. You should reach out and try to stay on good terms with all family members for your children's sake. Of course, your duty is to shield and protect your children from any relatives who may possibly harm them.

Family Traditions

Children also benefit from participating in rituals and traditions that show their family group is special. All families develop their own way of doing things that are different in every family. Families often celebrate holidays in special ways. Can you remember some things that your family did to celebrate holidays? We call these customs *family traditions*. Traditions are important because they help tie family members together. Traditions also organize the time that family members spend together in a positive way. We tie many of our oldest memories (good and bad) to special family events such as holidays and birthdays. Traditions include activities, special foods, and celebrations. There are three basic types of family traditions:

1. **Family Celebrations**: We do these things on special occasions such as birthdays, holidays, anniversaries, graduations, weddings, and so on.
2. **Family Events:** These are special activities that each family creates, such as trips or vacations, movie night, family meetings, eating out, reunions, and so on.
3. **Family Routines:** These are everyday patterns of how we do things such as mealtime, bedtime, wash day, pizza day, Saturday afternoons, and so on.

Families with the strongest ties have the most traditions. These rituals provide stability in the child's life, which is very comforting. They know what to expect. Traditions create opportunities for family members to make good memories that they will have for a lifetime. Such traditions are a source of strength that help family members feel good about themselves and each other.

Traditions connect us to the past and help link the generations together. They also provide a way to arrange our memories. These shared memories give children a sense of cultural identity that strongly connects them to their families. Learn your family traditions. Your children can get a lot from them. Even minor events can be lifetime memories in the making.

As a mother, you can start new family traditions. Do not ignore this wonderful gift. You can begin things that may last for generations to come.

Cultural Traditions

Some women in prison use their time to become reacquainted with their cultural and spiritual traditions. When used constructively, these traditions can be a source of strength when incarcerated women are reunified with their children. Helping your children develop a positive cultural identify is a tremendous gift you can give your child. Most cultures consider motherhood to be sacred since it means you are the creator of a human life. For many women, exploring and coming into contact with their traditional cultural ways is a giant step in their personal growth. It often means gaining pride in who you are. All cultures applaud responsible motherhood because it deals with the basic things we all share as human beings, such as love for our children.

Exercise 4-3: Family Relationships and Traditions

Directions: Read each question carefully and write in your best answer.

1. Why is it important that you keep a good relationship with your children's father(s)? List at least three reasons.

   ____

   ____

   ____

   ____

2. Explain why it is not a good idea to have your children carry messages back and forth between you and your child's father.

   ____

   ____

   ____

   ____

3. What are some of the good things your child can get from contact with his or her extended family (grandparents, cousins, aunts and uncles, and so on)?

   ____

   ____

   ____

   ____

4. What are three things you could do to reach out to other family members and develop good relationships with them?

____

____

____

____

5. Remember back to when you were about ten years old. Describe your favorite holiday. What things did you do to make it special?

____

____

____

____

6. What holidays do you want to make special for your kids? List them and then write down the special things you would like to do.

____

____

____

____

7. Write down any special foods that your family ate when you were a child. If you cannot think of any, what foods might you want to be special in your family now?

____

____

____

____

8. When your children grow up, what is one special family memory you would like them to have?

____

____

____

____

9. If your family were a sports team, what team name would it have? Are you satisfied with this name, or would you like to change it to something else?

____

____

____

____

Chapter 5

Special Issues

This chapter deals with several special issues confronting mothers today. The first lesson is about being able to talk with the father of your children. Whether you are married, divorced, or separated, it is important to try to establish a good working relationship with your child's father. Communication is the key. We provide some techniques to improve understanding along with ways to reduce potential conflicts.

The second lesson deals with school achievement. Mothers have a very important role in helping their children do well in school. We offer suggestions about what mothers can do to promote good school achievement. There is also a section on dealing with social service agencies and a discussion about retaining or losing custody of your child.

Lessons 5-3, 5-4, and 5-5 deal with major problems and trauma that can affect your ability to be an effective parents. Substance abuse, sexual abuse, and domestic violence are three roadblocks that often come together and that many incarcerated mothers must overcome. Facing these issues and getting the help you need can be the most important thing you do to help your children in the long run.

The final lesson in this chapter deals with the different needs of daughters and sons. For many women, having a daughter represents a second chance at life. They may be overly concerned that their daughter will repeat the same mistakes they made. Some women may pass along to their sons anger at men from past abuse. Feeling cheated in life themselves, some mothers may pressure their sons and daughters to be successful.

Many mothers feel more comfortable talking to their daughters than their sons. Raising a boy, especially alone, presents many special challenges for mothers. This lesson looks at this issue and gives several suggestions for raising a son today.

Lesson 5-1: Communication Skills

What Is Effective Communication?

Communication is the basis for all healthy relationships. By sharing experiences and expressing feelings, people are able to grow closer. We all want other people to understand us, and we want to understand them. Effective communication is the key to this shared understanding.

Communication is important when there are relationship problems. Good communication encourages problem-solving and helps in settling disagreements. Effective communication occurs when the other person receives and understands your intended message. The same basic rules apply whether you are trying to communicate with your child, an ex-husband, or a current boyfriend.

Listening: The Most Important Communication Skill

Most people think that talking is the most important communication skill. However, listening is much more important. Good listening sends a message of its own. It tells the other person that you respect him or her. Effective listening can prevent problems and misunderstandings. Several factors are involved in effective listening:

1. A good listener pays as much attention to the speaker's feelings as to the words.
2. A good listener pays attention to tone, expressions, and gestures.
3. A good listener shows respect by listening closely, even if she disagrees with what she is hearing.
4. A good listener checks out what she thinks she hears.
5. A good listener tries to understand the message completely before talking.
6. A good listener avoids anger, name-calling, or making fun of another.
7. A good listener knows that often people do not want a solution or answer; they just want to be heard and understood.

Active listening occurs when you take time to check out the other person's feelings. Active listening is probably the most important communication skill you can learn. It encourages people to open up and communicate better. It also helps people calm down. It is a way of showing respect for others. Active listening has four basic steps:

Steps in Active Listening

1. Listen for the feeling the other person is really expressing.
2. Connect the feeling to the events being talked about.
3. Tell the other person the feeling you think you heard them say and how it connects to the event.
4. Based on what the person says back, try to improve your description of his or her feelings.

Active listening is not just parroting back the same words the person spoke. Below are some examples of good active listening.

Statement: "It drives me crazy when the kids run around screaming and yelling."

Active listening response: "It must be really upsetting when the kids are such a handful."

In active listening, you do not offer a solution. You simply let the other persons know that you understand how they feel and why they feel that way.

Statement: "My boss is such a jerk. He constantly criticizes everything I do. Nothing is good enough for him. I hate his guts."

Active listening response: "Sounds like you're very angry at your boss for being so picky and unreasonable."

Statement: "I have tried everything to get that kid to pick up his clothes. If he leaves the bathroom filthy one more time, I'm going to scream."

Active listening response: "I hear you saying that you feel extremely frustrated because Reggie never follows directions."

Active listening takes a great deal of effort. Good active listening requires you to be alert and use your sensitivity to understand the speaker's feelings.

Assume the Best

Many of us go into situations thinking other people are out to hurt us. We may think they plan to put us down or make us feel bad. This, of course, is usually not the case with other family members. However, this negative attitude blocks communication. We may take every word and gesture as a sign of something bad. Research has shown that when you believe that the other person wants the best for you, your relationship is much better. Taking things that people say in the best possible light improves communication.

In most cases, other family members do want what is best for you, but they may be clumsy in how they show it. Look for good intentions. Be forgiving. Realize that most of the time, other family members are not the enemy and are doing the best they can. Try to give them the benefit of the doubt.

Self-Expression

Be as clear as you can be in your communications with others. Do not expect other people to read your mind. Many of us get angry when other people do not understand what we are trying to say. Since it is so clear to us, we think it should be clear to everyone else. Remember, most people have difficulty listening closely. Instead of listening, people are thinking about how they will answer. You may have to repeat things or say them in different ways so that other people can understand them.

One of the biggest blocks to effective communication is blame. Blaming immediately puts the other person on the defensive and ends all effective communication. Instead of trying to understand your point of view, the other person just tries to defend himself. If all you talk about is how bad the other person is, you have fallen into the blame trap.

One helpful way to reduce the blame is to limit the use of the word "you." Communication experts call this "sending I-messages." For example, instead of saying,

"**You** always bring the kids late," you can send an *I-message* instead: "**I** feel worried when the kids are not home on time, because **I** worry about what might have happened to them." It takes some practice to learn to send I-messages. The important thing to remember is to limit the use of the word "you" and to start sentences with the word "I." Also, do not let the word "you" sneak into the last part of the sentence such as "**I** get very upset when **you** act like a jerk." There are three features of a good I-message.

1. The message talks about the person's own feeling (I feel worried).
2. The message tells what starts the feeling (when the kids get home late).
3. The statement tells the reason for the feeling (because I worry about what might have happened to them).

Here are some examples of I-messages:

- "I feel upset when the kids are yelled at, because I remember how bad I felt when my mother yelled at me."
- "I feel bad when I hear my parents criticized because they mean so much to me."
- "I feel worthless when someone talks about how badly I did in school, because I tried as hard as I could."

Other Communication Tips

Always pick the right time and place to communicate. When someone is rushed or worried, that is not a good time to have an important talk. Choose a place that is private and free from noise and activity. For important things, schedule a special time to talk to make sure there are no time pressures or interruptions.

Be aware when your partner or child wants to talk to you. Take advantage of those times. Spending time alone, taking a walk, or riding in the car are excellent times to talk privately. Limiting television time also can increase chances to communicate.

It is best to take turns when talking. Listen fully to the other person before taking your turn. Do not cut in before he or she has finished.

Sometimes words fail us. Just taking the other person's hand or giving a hug may be the best message when emotions are very strong. Sometimes, it is best to take a break when feelings get intense. You can begin again later.

Voices and Viewpoints

Josephine says, "I give up. There's no way I can talk to my mother. All she wants to do is to blame me about things I've done in the past. She just can't get over it. There's no point in talking to her."

What do you think? Is Josephine right? Are there some people you just can't deal with? Is there anything you can do to try to get past the blame?

____

____

____

____

____

Things to Avoid

The following list includes several things that can cut off communication. Try to avoid doing these things:

1. Being sarcastic or disrespectful
2. Butting in before the other person is done talking
3. Ignoring the other person's feelings
4. Name-calling
5. Focusing on what you will say instead of listening to the other person
6. Using angry insults
7. Making their behavior sound worse by exaggerating
8. Being highly judgmental

Many of these communication-killers deal with being respectful and managing your feelings. It is important to listen first and control your wish to fight back before you have time to think. Exaggerations can be especially harmful. These usually begin with the words "You always" or "You never." Make sure you do not fall into these common traps. Good communication is very important.

Exercise 5-1: Communication Skills Practice

Active Listening Practice

Directions: Read each of the statements below carefully and then fill in an active listening response. This is what you might say back to the person talking to you.

Sample Statement: "I don't know why you never call me when you're going to be late. I always imagine that something terrible happened to you. I worry that you are dead and lying in some ditch."

Response: *"It sounds like you feel really upset and anxious when I'm late and do not call you."*

1. **Statement:** "You're so inconsiderate. You never bring the kids over to see me. All you want from me is my money."

Response: ____

____

____

____

2. **Statement:** "My mom never did anything for me. She was selfish, and all she cared about was herself. I was glad when she died."

Response: ____

____

____

____

3. **Statement:** "When the kids are very sick like this, I can barely stand it. It makes me feel so depressed."

Response: ____

____

____

____

4. **Statement:** "I don't care what we agreed; the kids have to stay with me over the holidays. I am not going to stay at home by myself feeling bad."

Response: ____

____

____

____

5. **Statement:** "No, I cannot give you any child support this month. I only worked a few days, and I need money to live on myself. You'd just waste the child support on yourself anyway."

Response: ____

____

____

____

I-Message Practice

Directions: Read each of the statements below carefully and then rewrite the statement as an *I-message*. This is how you can speak to someone in a way that might not make them as defensive.

Sample Statement: "Can't you ever stop nagging about my visits with the kids? I come as often as I can. I have to work all the time."

I-Message: *"I feel upset when we talk about my visits with the kids because I feel so guilty. I really want to be able to see them."*

1. **Statement:** "What is the matter with you? Look at these crummy grades. Are you stupid or something? Do you ever listen to what I tell you?"

I-Message: ____

____

____

____

2. **Statement:** "How much money have you spent this week running around with your friends? We are not going to have enough money for food or to pay the electric bill. Do you ever think about these things?"

I-Message: ____

____

____

____

3. **Statement:** "If your mother says one more bad thing about the kids, I do not know what I am going to do. She should mind her own business. She is not raising those kids; I am."

I-Message: ____

____

____

____

4. **Statement:** "What do you mean you're tired? You are always too tired when I want to do something. You never seem too tired to go out when your buddies call."

I-Message: ____

____

____

____

5. **Statement:** "Why do you always have to complain about my mother? She never does anything to you. You are just jealous because the kids like her better than your mother."

I-Message:____

____

____

____

Lesson 5-2: Working with the School and Social Service Agencies

Working Effectively with Your Child's School

The Mother's Role in School Achievement

How you do as a parent greatly affects how well your child does in school. The more the mother supports school, the better the child typically does. Success today depends a lot on school achievement. Schooling is very important in getting a good job. Although some families do not believe school is important, it is very difficult to succeed today without an education. Encourage your children to attend school regularly, go to each class, and complete high school. Even while you are incarcerated, your encouragement about school attendance is important.

For many incarcerated mothers, school was difficult. Even as adults, they may have bad feelings about school because of their past experiences. Do not let your past feelings hurt your child's chance to do well in school. Even if your school memories are bad, you still can encourage your children.

In some neighborhoods, doing well in school is discouraged and is labeled as trying to "act white." This is a harmful idea. It may discourage African-American and other children from doing their best in school. Remember, doing well in school is color-blind. All cultures value creativity and intelligence. The mother's job is to help her children appreciate their cultural identity while gaining the knowledge they need to succeed. Mothers may also want to look into adult education programs to improve their own skills and job prospects. The example they set will strongly affect their children's choices.

Reinforcing School Rules and Expectations

Some children will try to get their parents to fight with their teachers. They will try to convince their parents that the teacher is unfair, the homework is too long, and the tests are too hard. While you should be supportive of your child, do not fall into this trap. It is best if parents and teachers present a united front. You always should make the teacher an ally. Avoid fights or conflicts with school staff, and support school rules at home. You can help your children by making sure they are always clean and well-dressed in school. (This does not mean dressed in expensive clothes, either.) This sends a message that you value your kids. Your kids will be treated better.

Voices and Viewpoints

Teresa says, "I think school is entirely up to the kids. They need to take responsibility. I shouldn't have to mess with keeping track of everything."

Darlene says, "I do not want my son showing off in school and kissing up to the teachers. The other kids will think he's trying to be white or something."

What do you think? Should kids take all the responsibility for school? Do you think doing well in school is "acting white"? Explain why you feel that way.

____

____

____

____

____

____

____

____

Ask the teachers for suggestions about school-related problems. Tell the teachers that you do not want your child to be a problem for them and you will do anything they suggest to help your child improve his schoolwork. Teachers are professionals and have a wide range of experience with children. Your expectations for your child's achievement should match those of the school. Low expectations stop children from achieving all they can. You can reinforce school rules and expectations by carefully reading over all the materials the teacher sends home.

Do not make excuses for any misbehavior or try to blame someone else—the teacher, the school, other kids, and so forth. Help your children learn to accept responsibility for their behavior and choices by telling them that they must accept the consequences for mistakes. Tell them about your own experiences.

When you are no longer in prison, there are many things you can do to show support for your child's schooling, such as:

- Attend all school open houses.
- Schedule school conferences to regularly meet with teachers.
- Give the teacher feedback on how things are going at home.
- Always treat teachers with the utmost respect. Show concern for their point of view, and thank them for their help.
- Keep the lines of communication open between home and school.

Monitoring Your Child's Progress

Some parents wait until report cards come out and then are shocked by their child's poor grades. If you are doing your job as a mother, your child's grades should never be a surprise. Through constant communication with the teacher and checking homework and tests, you should have a good idea of how your child is doing. Some parents arrange to get a weekly report from the teacher so that they always know how things are going. If this sounds like a lot of work, you're right. Raising children is a full-time job that takes great effort.

If your child is having severe behavior or learning problems in school, he or she may need counseling or other professional help. Listen carefully to the teacher's suggestions. Then, follow through on getting your child whatever help he or she needs.

Homework, Tests, and Assignments

To do well in school, children must work on certain tasks every day. First, you must be sure that your children attend school regularly and are on time to school. Mothers may not be aware that their children are skipping school or certain classes. Friends of your children may influence them to cut classes. Remember, peer pressure is very strong. The good communication skills mentioned in the previous chapter are critical in this area.

Children need to pay attention to the teacher when he or she explains things in class. They need to complete all their work in class. They need to study for tests. They also need to do their homework. These are all the things they must do to get good grades, and they should become everyday habits. Never assume that these things will happen automatically. Be active, and set up a regular schedule for homework and studying. You should also know when your child is having tests and that she is fully prepared. Parents can help children study for tests by calling out weekly spelling words. They can also ask their children questions to see if they know their other subjects.

By keeping in close contact with the school, you should also know how well your child is doing in class. You should reward your child for completing tasks at school with praise as well as privileges.

Reading with Your Child

Reading to your child is one of the best ways to encourage good school performance. Since reading is the most important academic skill, anything that improves it will help your child do better in school. Reading also affects feelings. When a mother reads to her child, they form a stronger bond. As children's reading skills improve, their self-esteem increases. Because of the individual attention, reading together is usually fun for children. Children can connect these good feelings to other school activities.

Reading together:

1. Strengthens the mother's relationship with her child
2. Increases the child's vocabulary
3. Helps children think and come up with ideas
4. Increases general knowledge
5. Encourages independent reading
6. Improves reading skills for all school subjects

Set up a regular time to read with your child. If your facility allows it, you might be able to begin this before reunification by sending stories on audiotapes. Some facilities have a special program to help with this. Check out this possibility.

You will probably need to get some help in choosing books that are best for your child. Teachers and librarians can help you select the right books. When you are out of prison, visit your local public library regularly and learn about the services that it offers. The public library can assist you and your child in a variety of ways. Besides having books, CDs, and videos, most libraries have Internet availability, puppet shows, parties, and story hours for young children. When you are released, plan regular trips to the public library to check out new books for your children. To improve your own reading skills, you might want to look into adult education or literacy programs. Many of these are often held at the library.

Exercise 5-2a: Dealing with School Issues

Directions: Read each question carefully and write in your best answer below.

1. Think back to when you were twelve years old. How did you feel about school back then? Describe your feelings below.

____

____

____

____

2. Can you remember any of your teachers? Tell about a teacher you liked and one that you did not like.

____

____

____

____

3. How do you want your children to feel about school? What are some things that you can do to help them feel that way?

____

____

____

____

4. What are some ways that you can keep an eye on how your child is doing in school? List three things that you can do.

____

____

____

____

5. What are the things your children need to do daily to get good grades? How can you help them do these things?

____

____

____

____

6. While growing up, what was your family's attitude toward school and education?

____

____

____

____

7. Did you drop out? Are there things that you need to do to further your own education? What steps might you take toward improving your own educational experiences now? How might this influence your children?

____

____

____

____

Working Effectively with Social Service Agencies

Protective Services and Reunification

Protective services or other social service agencies will supervise many families. Children who have spent time in foster care or in the temporary care of a relative during a parent's incarceration may have a caseworker who will develop a plan to reunite the family. One of the first steps is often a requirement that you contribute financially to the child's care. Then, there may be a period of visitation, either supervised or unsupervised. The reunification plan is something to explore as soon as possible before you are released.

It is easy to become upset when dealing with a large agency that has many rules. Things may not always seem fair. However, mothers must always keep their main goal in mind—the return of their children. As with school teachers, try to make your caseworker your ally. Avoid getting into any fights that might slow down reunification.

Performance Agreements

In some states, the part of the reunification plan that describes all the things you have to do to regain custody is called a *performance agreement*. In it, you agree to do certain things. Performance agreements are based on the caseworker's assessment of the family's needs. Depending on the assessment, you might be required to do things such as seek counseling for yourself or your children, attend AA or NA groups, get job training or maintain a job, attend school conferences, maintain a safe and appropriate living environment, and provide adequate supervision for your children. Your performance agreement may also have some special requirements based on your individual needs.

Often, mothers may feel that these performance agreements are too bossy and tell them how to live their lives. They may not feel that all the conditions are necessary. Even if you disagree with the conditions, it is important that you do everything in your power to try to meet them to avoid others accusing you of having a bad attitude. You need to bend over backward to make sure that you do everything that is written in the agreement. Do not look for excuses. Always go the extra mile to try to get these things done.

Many women who have been in prison have a special problem with authority figures. They may also have problems managing their anger or dealing with frustration. You may seek help for this problem while in prison or when you are released.

Foster Care and Custody Issues

Most children of incarcerated parents stay with relatives. Some, however, are placed in the custody of the state, usually in foster care. Mothers with children in foster care may risk losing custody. Some states have rules that child welfare agencies must try to terminate parental rights if a child had been in foster care for fifteen out of the last twenty-two months. About one out of every ten women in prison has a child in foster care. Women who have their babies in prison and do not have family members to take the child are often in jeopardy of losing custody.

Caseworkers can ask for exceptions to these rules. That is why it is so important that you show your caseworker that you are concerned and attached to your children. Make sure you do everything to try to get visitation with your children. If you cannot, make sure that you write, send cards or tapes, and try to communicate as much as possible. The caseworker needs to know that continued contact with you is in the best interest of your children.

Facing the Loss of Child Custody

Tougher foster care guidelines have resulted in many parents losing custody of their children. We all know that sometimes, no matter how much an incarcerated mother loves her child and has worked to be a good parent, the court may feel it is best to place the child elsewhere.

It is important to think about this possibility and prepare for it. If it should happen, it will be like other major losses in your life. After the shock wears off, you should expect to have feelings of loneliness and emptiness at first. Feelings of loss may lead to some disorganization and problems getting things done for a while. In time, you will regroup and move on with your life in spite of the painful memories.

You also could promise yourself that you will get through this, if it should happen. It also might help if you can tell yourself that was not because you did not try. We all want to feel that we did our best to take care of our children. Some women, however, have so much pain and disappointment in their lives that they lose hope. They might not try to hold on to their children because they feel it will be even harder to let go when, sooner or later, they fail.

If there is any message in this program, it is that being incarcerated does not make anyone a bad person, and change is always possible. Losing custody does not make anyone a bad person, and it does not have to wreck your future. This not the time to blame yourself, but to move into "survival mode."

People can learn to make better choices and gain more control of their lives. We can all take some comfort and pride in making our lives better. Even children who are lost may someday grow up, look up a parent, and benefit from the knowledge that you can positively change your life.

A Word about Visits

Visits can be very emotional for both you and your children. Many mothers and children get very nervous. Often, both have unrealistic hopes that such a stressful event will be fun. You cannot change the past. The present is very hard, but you can work toward a better future by taking one small step at a time.

Try not to feel hurt if your child hangs back, is quiet, acts angry, or misbehaves. Your only goal is to give the consistent message to your child that you are okay and that you care for him or her. If it is possible, do some activity with your child during the visit such as reading a book or drawing a picture. This can help the visit go better.

Developing a Positive Relationship

Many of the things mentioned above about dealing with teachers also apply to your caseworker. Treat your caseworker with respect. Do not let your pride get in your way. Ask for advice and help when appropriate. Avoid power struggles, and control your frustration and anger. Never avoid visits, and always be on time for appointments. If you start to get your feelings hurt, take a deep breath and just listen calmly. Working effectively with social service agencies is a major test of your ability to function as a mature adult. Success will depend largely on your patience and self-control. This is often very hard, but your kids are worth any amount of trouble.

Exercise 5-2b: Working with Social Service Agencies

Directions: Read each question carefully and write in your best answer below.

1. What are some of the reasons it is important to have a good working relationship with social service agencies?

____

____

____

____

2. If your performance agreement requires you to go to counseling, and you feel that this is not necessary, what should you do?

____

____

____

____

3. Which is most important to you—making sure that you always are being treated fairly, or keeping custody of your children?

____

____

____

____

4. If your car breaks down and you have appointments to keep for your performance agreement, what are some things that you could do?

____

____

____

____

5. What are the main barriers that women have in working effectively with social service agencies?

____

____

____

____

6. What are some things you might do to prepare yourself for the possible loss of custody of your children?

____

____

____

____

7. What are some reasons that a woman might not try to keep or regain custody of her children?

____

____

____

____

8. If an incarcerated friend just lost custody of her child, what would you say to her?

____

____

____

____

Illustration by John DiCiesare, *Shielding the Darkness*

Lesson 5-3: Women and Substance-Abuse Issues

Impacts of Substance Abuse

Important Note to Participants

If you have a substance-abuse addiction, you may ask for a referral to a behavioral health professional or program specializing in substance abuse treatment.

Individual Impact

Most women serving prison sentences today have drug-related charges. Many women were also victims of childhood physical and sexual abuse. Physically and sexually abused girls are twice as likely to drink or use drugs than those not abused. Sexually abused girls are also much more likely to abuse substances earlier, more often, and in greater quantities. Having a poor relationship with your parents is another factor that leads to a greater likelihood for alcohol or drug abuse. For these reasons, you want to work hard to have a good relationship with your own daughters and keep them safe.

More than half of all women inmates report some type of substance abuse. Incarcerated women have higher rates of substance abuse than incarcerated men do. Many incarcerated women committed their offense under the influence of drugs or alcohol.

Impact on Children

Parental substance abuse, of course, has a very negative effect on children. Mothers who abuse drugs or alcohol are unable to properly supervise, protect, or care for their children. Substance abuse interferes with their judgment. Child neglect, abandonment, and even abuse can be the results of poor judgment. In such situations, children often develop long-term depression, anxiety, and anger. Children need a stable caring home, something that a substance-abusing mother just cannot provide.

The First Step

The first step in getting help for a substance abuse problem is to admit that you have a problem and need help. Breaking through all the defenses and denial that most people

Voices and Viewpoints

Sheena says, "I don't need nobody to help me. I can quit using drugs any time I want. It's nobody's business but my own."

Essie says, "I give up. I tried three times, and it didn't do no good. I just can't quit."

What do you think? Do you believe Sheena can really quit on her own? Why or why not? Do you think three times is trying enough for your kids' sake?

____

____

____

____

____

build up over time requires a lot of courage. Many women kid themselves that they have control over their substance abuse and can stop anytime they want. Admitting to having the problem requires a major change in the way you think about everything, especially yourself. For most people, this realization is a life-changing experience. Things never look quite the same again.

Once you realize that there is a problem, the next step is to make a commitment to do something about it.

The Importance of Getting Help

More than two-thirds of incarcerated women with substance abuse problems have tried some form of treatment. Recovery from a substance abuse disorder is often very difficult. Maintaining sobriety over time is even harder. Relapses are common, and people often have to start again to get the help they need. If you have a substance abuse problem, now is the time to begin your recovery for your own sake, and especially for the sake of your children.

Do not be discouraged if you have tried treatment in the past and it has not worked. The important thing is to keep trying. Research shows that treatment can cut drug abuse in half, reduce criminal activity by up to 80 percent, and reduce arrests by up to 64 percent. Sometimes it may take many, many tries before treatment has positive effects. Do not get discouraged.

If substance abuse counseling, treatment groups, or self-help groups are available in your correctional facility, seek them out immediately and participate as fully as possible. Substance abuse treatment does work. It can help in a variety of ways in getting your life back together, and especially in being able to relate to your children.

What is Effective Substance Abuse Treatment?

Effective substance abuse treatment for women generally includes the following aspects:

- Treatment must deal with all of the person's needs, not just alcohol or drug addiction.
- Substance abuse treatment should be part of a plan that also includes help for domestic violence, physical abuse, and sexual abuse.
- Ideally, your treatment should be assessed often and changed to meet your current needs.
- Attending twelve-step/self-help groups every day or several times a week is an important part of treatment.
- Getting treatment for a long enough time is important.
- Counseling and behavioral therapy are critical parts of treatment.
- Substance abusing individuals with other problems, such as depression, should be treated so all the counselors and doctors can work together.
- Withdrawal alone does not change long-term substance use.
- You should receive regular drug tests to be monitored for possible substance use during treatment.
- Treatment should include assessment and counseling for HIV/AIDS, hepatitis B and C, tuberculosis, and other infectious diseases.
- Recovery is a long-term process and requires continual care.

Types of Treatment

The following are the main types of treatment currently in use for substance abuse problems.

- *Hospitalization (Detoxification)*: Some individuals require an initial stay in the hospital to help them rid their bodies of the substances they have been abusing. This is a short-term, mostly medical activity that sets the stage for future treatment efforts. Most incarcerated women have already been detoxified while in custody.
- *Residential Substance Abuse Treatment*: In this approach, the woman stays in a residential setting and receives her treatment there. This is not a medical facility and is usually appropriate for people who have not been able to succeed in outpatient treatment. Such programs usually last from one week to twenty-eight days, although some programs of ninety day and longer are occasionally available. Residential programs help remove women from their usual surroundings, which may have led them to use.
- *Halfway Houses*: Many women live in halfway houses while they are trying to put their lives together. A halfway house is a facility where several women live together in a supervised setting while undergoing rehabilitation. Some women go to halfway houses after leaving prison or the hospital. They are places that help women readjust to the outside world and perhaps get a job. Halfway houses offer an orderly, supportive, and caring place to live. This is often a good beginning for women leaving prison.
- *Partial Hospitalization*: People with severe substance abuse problems may require treatment several hours a day, most days of the week. However, they do not need to be in a medical facility twenty-four hours a day. Partial hospitalization is a very structured and intense daytime treatment program.
- *Intensive Outpatient Treatment*: Intensive outpatient treatment involves spending several hours, and perhaps several days or weeks, in treatment activities. It can resemble partial hospitalization, but services are not quite as intense or frequent.
- *Outpatient Treatment*: Most outpatient treatment programs involve attending individual or group sessions or some combination of both, once every week or two. A professional substance-abuse counselor provides the treatment in this setting.
- *Twelve-Step and Support Groups*: These are primarily self-help groups, based on the Alcoholics Anonymous (AA) and Narcotics Anonymous (NA) model. Generally, members of the group, not professionals, run these groups. Usually

people attend several meetings a week. Most people in other types of treatment also use these groups to enhance their recovery.

The following techniques are used in a variety of treatment settings, including inpatient, outpatient, and residential:

- *Cognitive-Behavioral Therapy*: This approach helps people change their thinking about situations that lead to substance abuse. It also helps them recognize, avoid, and manage situations where they are likely to abuse substances. This workbook is based on a cognitive-behavioral approach—it helps you learn to have thoughts that are helpful and to realize those thoughts that would be best to change.
- *Motivational Interviewing*: This approach recognizes that people are at many different stages of change. This approach uses many different interventions to help increase women's motivation to change.
- *Contingency Management*: This approach uses rewards to encourage people not to use drugs or alcohol. In this approach, persons must first do something constructive such as attend AA or NA meetings, get screened for drugs, or attend a therapy session to get something they want, such as unsupervised visitation or a release pass from a halfway house.

Staying Clean and Sober

If you have substance abuse problems, make sure that your reunification plan addresses in detail how and where you will get treatment and help for this problem when you are released.

Exercise 5-3: Women and Substance Abuse

Directions: Read each question carefully and write down your best answer.

1. How is substance abuse related to the large increase in the number of women who are incarcerated?

____

____

____

____

2. How does substance abuse interfere with your ability to be a good parent to your children?

____

____

____

____

3. What are three elements of an effective substance abuse treatment program?

____

____

____

____

4. What are three of the most common types of substance abuse treatment?

____

____

____

____

5. What is the most important first step in recovery from substance abuse? Why is it so important?

____

____

____

____

Lesson 5-4: Sexual Abuse

Sexual Abuse and Incarcerated Women

About two-thirds of incarcerated women have experienced some type of sexual abuse in their lives. Child sexual abuse is the use of a child for any form of sexual activity by an adult or adolescent. It includes a variety of things such as fondling, sexual intercourse, oral-genital contact, and exposure to pornography or a sexual act. It is a betrayal of trust by someone with power over the child. A sexual abuse incident usually means that others in the household (most often the child's mother) failed to protect the child. The abusers are typically family members, friends of the parents or their older children, acquaintances who visit the home, or other close friends of the family such as the mother's boyfriend or fiancée. Abuse by strangers does take place, but not as often as abuse by someone you know.

Symptoms and Impact of Sexual Abuse

Childhood sexual abuse can affect women in many different ways. It increases the likelihood of substance abuse and depression and is often associated with post-traumatic stress disorder (PTSD). PTSD is primarily an anxiety disorder. Besides feeling anxious and insecure, people with PTSD often mentally remove themselves from traumatic situations by "spacing out" in a process called *dissociation.*

Depending on how bad the abuse was, it may lead to suicide attempts and such self-destructive things such as cutting your legs, arms, or wrists or burning yourself with cigarettes. Children who are sexually abused often engage in sexual behavior at earlier ages. As teenagers, female abuse victims often have babies sooner than other girls do.

In addition, sexually abused women often have to deal with issues such as:

- **Low self-esteem**: Sexually abused women may feel that they are "damaged goods" and not as good as other people. They often feel rejected or hated by God. This may make getting support from their church a problem.
- **Guilt**: They may feel that the abuse was somehow their fault. They may also feel guilty because the abuse caused problems in the family. Families may blame them.
- **Lack of trust**: Sexually abused women often have problems trusting others since sexual abuse is foremost a betrayal by the very people who were supposed to take care of you.

- **Relationship problems**: Some of the other issues spill into this area since abused women often have problems establishing an intimate relationship in which men treat them with respect and care. Women may grow up thinking that all men are abusive or that no one better would want them.
- **Intense anger**: Anger (primarily at the abuser and the people who should have provided protection) can often erupt in other situations, causing problems.
- **Grief**: If the father was the abuser, women often grieve for the love and concern that they wanted from their mothers, who chose to accommodate the father's desires instead of providing for their child's safety and well-being.
- **Sexual problems**: Sexual abuse disrupts normal development, and the effects of the abuse causes problems in adult sexual and intimate relationships.
- **Flashbacks**: Some women experience sudden intense and overwhelming negative feelings (such as panic attacks) related to the abuse. Objects or events that are related to the abuse experience trigger these feelings. They may continue throughout a woman's life if not treated.
- **Swiss cheese memory**: Many, if not most, sexually abused women do not remember extended periods of their childhood when the abuse was especially frequent or painful. Like Swiss cheese, their memory is full of holes.

The Impact of Sexual Abuse on Being an Effective Parent

Research has shown that sexually abused mothers often have much less confidence in their parenting. They also frequently view themselves more negatively as parents. They may punish too much and have less emotional control when dealing with their kids. Much of their time and energy is drained away trying to cope with the bad feelings stemming from their abuse experiences. These are some good reasons why it is important for you to deal with your abuse issues. When you feel better, you can be a better parent. Very few sexually abused women abuse their own children in this way. However, some survivors of abuse who have not sought treatment may not adequately protect their children from abuse.

Stages of Recovery: Being a Survivor

Recovery from sexual-abuse trauma often takes time and cannot be rushed. Below are descriptions of many of the stages most women go through in the process of recovery. Not all women go through all of the stages. The stages overlap, and their order may be jumbled. Many women frequently come back to earlier stages to complete some "unfinished business." The most important thing is that you start on this road to recovery as soon as possible and that you see yourself for what you are—a survivor.

- *Denial*: Many people stay in this stage for years after the actual abuse has ended. Many women develop addictive or compulsive behaviors to cover up the bad feeling from the abuse.
- *Making the decision to heal*: This happens when the woman recognizes how abuse has affected her life and makes a decision to heal despite the fear of facing terrible memories and realities.
- *Anger*: Some label anger the "backbone of healing" and "a vehicle for recovery." When women become more aware of how abuse has affected their lives, one of the first reactions is one of intense anger. This is expected and is a natural part of the healing process. They often aim their anger at the abuser. Often there is even more anger at their mother for failing to protect them. This anger comes from the strong sense of betrayal.
- *Remember what really happened*: In this stage, women break the secrecy that usually comes along with sexual abuse. Often encouraged by their families, many women push back their abuse memories. Remembering can trigger flashbacks and even physical sensations from the past. Telling another person the story has a powerful healing effect, as does knowing that other women have experienced and survived similar things. Participation in a group of childhood abuse survivors can be a life-changing experience.
- *Crisis/confusion*: As awareness grows and old hurts are brought up, the woman may have periods of anxiety, panic, and fear.
- *Understand that it was not your fault*: As child, you may have believed that the abuse was somehow your fault. It is important to place the blame where it belongs—directly on the abuser. This is called *relinquishing the guilt.*
- *Reach out/Speak out*: At some stage in their recovery, many women have a need to reach out and express their story. They also may want to read or write about the abuse. Individual counseling and/or joining a support group can play a critical role in recovery. Some women may choose to prosecute or take other legal action against their abuser.
- *Grieve and feel depressed*: At this stage, survivors recall the hurtful messages from their abuser. Many may feel very depressed, powerless, and unable to make positive changes. Identifying the triggers for depression, getting support from others, and challenging any self-defeating beliefs can keep you from feeling overwhelmed. Counseling is often needed in this stage of recovery.

Voices and Viewpoints

Helen says, "My stepdad messed with me the whole time I lived at home. Ever since I was little. I know my mother must have known. Why didn't she do anything to stop him? I hated him, but she was worse. She betrayed me. How am I supposed to feel about her now?"

Tina says, "My caseworker said that I couldn't leave my little girl alone with Derrick or she would put her in foster care. I know Derrick got in trouble with his own daughter, but he's better now. She's my daughter, and I should be able to do what I want."

What do you think? How should Helen feel about her mother? How would you feel? Does Tina have a point? What would you do if you were her?

____

____

____

____

____

____

____

- *Clarify emotions and reorganize*: In this very important stage, women often become much clearer about what happened and why. Women start to make many positive changes in their thinking and attitudes. They again develop a sense of trust in others and themselves. They learn from the past, examine the present, and plan for the future. They see themselves as survivors—not victims. They move from merely existing to actively living.
- *Self-forgiveness*: Some people say that you have to forgive your abuser or those who did not protect you in order to heal. This is not true. It is not necessary for you to forgive these people. What is important is self-forgiveness. It is important

to forgive yourself for any past actions you feel ashamed of or any negative behavior that you used to cope with your abuse.

- *Move on*: This is the stage of finding peace. At this time, many women make decisions about how they will relate to their abuser and/or mother in the future if they choose to have a relationship with them. In this stage, they make a shift from focusing on the negative experiences of the past to shaping positive plans for the future. Coping skills learned earlier now help survivors move ahead. Women often make decisions to protect themselves from all future attempts at abuse, and they commit themselves to protect their children from the pain of abuse.

Getting the Help You Need

Mothers who are survivors of sexual abuse need to seek out counseling and support-group assistance to work through the abuse trauma. Make sure your reunification plan says where and how you will get help with this issue when you are released. Help is often available through your local community mental health or women's center. You also can call the National Sexual Assault Hotline at 1-800-656-HOPE to find resources in your community.

Protecting Your Own Children

Some experts believe that sexual abuse tends to run in families. It is hard to tell if this is true because of all the other factors involved. In any case, it is very important that you do all you can to protect your children from this possible harm. Below are the key steps in protecting children from sexual abuse.

- *Become educated about abuse*: More than 90 percent of children are sexually abused by people the family knows and trusts.
- *Reduce opportunities for abuse*: Always make sure someone you trust properly supervises your child. Whenever possible, do not leave your child alone with other adults such as sports coaches or club leaders. Offer to be a helper or chaperone.
- *Talk to your child about abuse*: Make sure your child understands what abuse is and knows that it is all right to tell you if something happens.
- *Keep alert*: Do not expect obvious signs. Act when you first suspect something. You do not need absolute proof to act. Trust your instincts. If something seems wrong, do not gloss over it. Pay attention to your children's nightmares and when your children tell you they do not like someone. Do not be too busy to

investigate. Believe your children. If a child starts touching herself frequently, this is a warning sign.

- *Know what to do*: Know where to get help and how to report abuse. Call Childhelp USA National Child Abuse Hotline (1-800-4-A-CHILD), or contact the National Children's Alliance at www.nca-online.org or 1-800-239-9950.

Finally, be very, very careful about leaving your children alone with stepfathers, boyfriends, or older adolescents. Never leave your children with anyone who might abuse alcohol or drugs while you are gone. Substance abuse may cause persons to do things they would not normally consider doing. Professional childcare facilities may cost money, but they generally are safer.

Exercise 5-4: Sexual Abuse

Directions: Read each question carefully and write down your best answer.

1. When a girl is sexually abused, whose fault is it? If the girl was flirty or sexually active, should she share the blame?

 ____

 ____

 ____

 ____

2. What are some of the major symptoms of sexual abuse?

 ____

 ____

 ____

 ____

3. What are the most important things you can do to break the cycle of abuse and protect your children?

____

____

____

____

4. What are some things that you think could really help you in recovering from sexual abuse?

____

____

____

____

5. How does sexual abuse affect your ability to parent your children effectively? How can you protect them from sexual abuse?

____

____

____

____

Lesson 5-5: Domestic Violence

Important Note to Facilitator and Participants

This is another lesson that may trigger strong emotions from some participants. Be prepared to deal with these feelings and channel them constructively as part of the recovery process. A referral to a mental health professional specializing in domestic violence may be necessary for participants who have significant trouble processing this material.

Identifying Domestic Violence

Domestic violence consists of emotional, physical, or sexual abuse by someone in an intimate or family relationship with the victim. Domestic violence is an abuse of power. The abuser controls and torments the victim through threats, intimidation, and physical violence. It is terrorism, plain and simple.

Among incarcerated women, experts estimate that one-half to two-thirds of them are survivors of domestic violence. Most victims of domestic violence are women and most perpetrators are men. However, domestic violence takes place in both heterosexual as well as same-sex relationships.

Domestic violence can occur in any of the following forms:

- **Physical:** Punching slapping, pushing, hitting, kicking, biting, and so forth
- **Psychological:** Name-calling, giving insults, constantly criticizing, belittling, making accusations
- **Sexual:** Being forced into unwanted sexual activity, rape
- **Threats:** Verbally being told that you will be harmed, threatening to hurt or take away the children, threatening suicide
- **Intimidation:** Using gestures and looks, smashing things as a form of threat
- **Isolation:** Being kept away from friends, family, and outside supports; having to account for all time away from home
- **Economic:** Not being allowed to work or have control of your own money (even money that you earn), having to get permission to spend money, and being forced to account for every penny

Perpetrators of domestic violence have several of the characteristics listed below. Women should be aware that potential partners who show these features run a very high risk of being abusive.

- Abuses alcohol or drugs
- Committed abuse early in the relationship or with previous partners
- Is intensely jealous and needs to control everything
- Was abused as a child or there was domestic violence in his home
- Is easily frustrated and has a violent temper
- Is cruel to animals
- Has low self-esteem
- Blames others for problems
- Sees violence as a solution to problems
- Is preoccupied with weapons, violence, or pornography
- Wants you with him all the time and wants all your attention

Effects of Domestic Violence on Children

Living in a home where there is domestic violence is extremely stressful. It can have many harmful effects on children. Some of the most common dangers include:

- Greatly increased chance for being neglected or abused
- Increased risk of being indirectly injured or hurt trying to protect their mother
- Higher risks of alcohol/drug abuse and behavior problems
- Increased risk for stress-related disorders, both mental (such as depression) and physical (for example, headaches or stomach pain)
- Interference with school performance
- Increased risk for committing domestic violence as adults for boys who witness it
- Emotional problems including anxiety, guilt, fear, and poor self-esteem
- Relationship problems, especially related to a lack of respect for women, or the inability to stand up for oneself

The Cycle of Violence

Most domestic violence follows a predictable cycle as illustrated below. Frustration or substance abuse fuels abusive episodes. Following the abuse, there is often a period of making up. The abuser may apologize, beg to be taken back, cry, threaten suicide, or make lavish promises never to do it again. The abuser also may try to say that abuse was just a minor thing or even deny that it even happened. In many cases, the abuser blames the victim for the behavior, saying she nagged or upset him. A honeymoon period may follow, and abuse does not occur for a while. The abuser may even try to make up with gifts or kind acts. The victim often begins to think that maybe the abuse will not happen again.

The next phase starts when tension begins to build again. The abuser's temper starts to get out of control once more. The victim tries to calm the abuser by walking on eggshells. She may cater to the abuser's every whim. However, nothing seems to be enough. This stage reaches its peak when the tension erupts into another violent act.

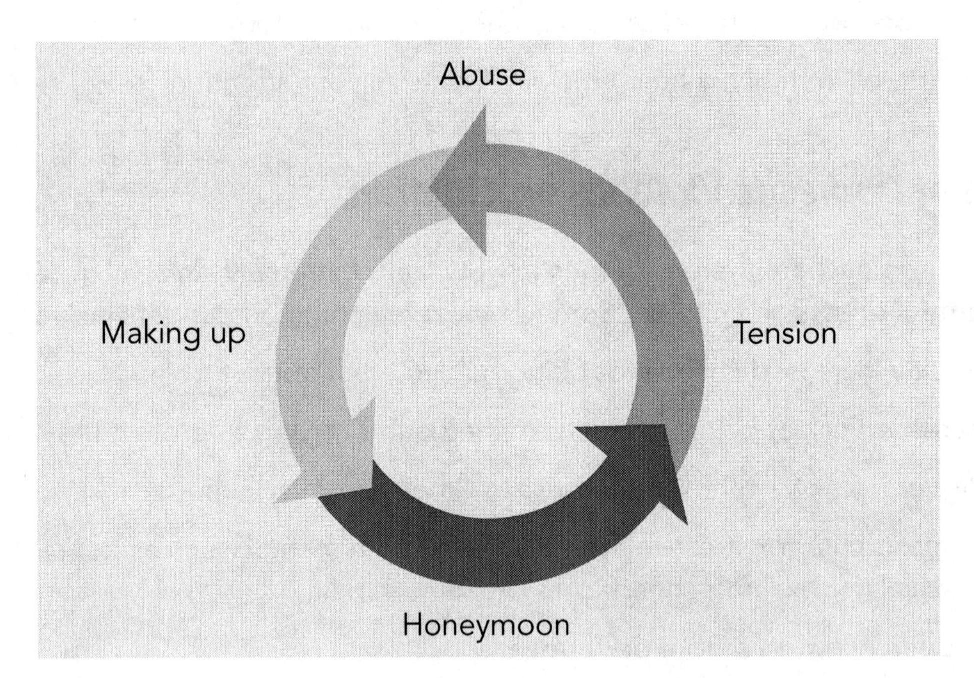

Barriers to Leaving an Abusive Relationship

Most people wonder why women who are victims of domestic violence simply do not leave the abuser. The truth is that it is very difficult to leave for a variety of reasons. These barriers to leaving include:

- **Fear of Injury or Death:** Leaving many abusers can be extremely dangerous, perhaps even fatal. Women may also be fearful of losing their children or putting them in danger by trying to leave.

Voices and Viewpoints

Selena says, "Enrique isn't so bad. He slaps me sometimes, but only when I got it coming. If I watch my mouth he treats me good."

Althea says, "Ain't no man going to hit me. I do not care if I have to live alone. I just won't stand for it."

What do you think? What kind of relationships do Selena and Enrique have? Is that what you want in your life? Do you agree with Althea or not? Why?

____

____

____

____

____

- **Isolation:** Abusers may frequently isolate victims of domestic violence from their friends, family members, and other sources of support.
- **Financial Issues:** Frequently, the abuser does not allow victims to have money, cars, credit cards, or other resources.
- **Individual Beliefs:** Some women strongly believe that any sort of a relationship is better than none. They also may believe that they simply cannot survive on their own. They may believe that all men treat women this way or that they are not good enough to find someone better. There is no evidence whatsoever that survivors "want to be abused" or "ask for it."
- **Hope:** It is very difficult to give up a relationship that once may have been very good. Many women still "love" or have positive feelings for the abuser. In addition, it is easy to cling to the unrealistic hope that the relationship will get better. Many women want to believe the abuser's promises. They may also have feelings of gratitude if the abuser helped them escape an abusive parent.
- **Community Services:** The lack of community support and services may make a woman feel as if there is no one to help.

- **Religious, Cultural, and Societal Values:** Some women are taught to be submissive in accordance with certain values or religious beliefs. They may blame themselves for the abuse. Some women feel they do not have the "right" to challenge their partner's authority. They may feel this way because the abuser makes all the money. Others may think or be told that it would be a "sin" to leave or not obey the abuser.

What Kind of Help Do Women Need?

The first issue to address is always safety. A domestic violence victim must develop a comprehensive protection plan that allows for a safe escape from dangerous situations. This plan might involve getting a court order or injunction, calling the police, or fleeing to a safe place. Many women use the domestic violence shelters in their communities. Others may go to the home of a friend or relative. Once you have addressed your safety, the longer-term goals of treatment include:

- Helping the woman identify how abuse has affected her life
- Helping the woman believe that she can survive without her partner and that she can build a satisfying life alone (empowerment)
- Regaining independence and securing training and employment
- Reconnecting with supports and resources
- As necessary, arranging for additional services to:
    - — Build self-esteem and confidence
    - — Treat depression or anxiety
    - — Address substance abuse
    - — Address sexual abuse (current or childhood)
    - — Develop relationship skills (changing dependency patterns, learning to speak up for herself)

To access treatment service in your community, call the National Domestic Violence Hotline at 1-800-799-7233 (SAFE) or e-mail ndvh@ndvh.org.

Stages of Recovery for Domestic Violence Survivors

Domestic abuse survivors usually progress through several stages in learning to deal with their situations in a more effective way. These stages overlap and do not always follow each other.

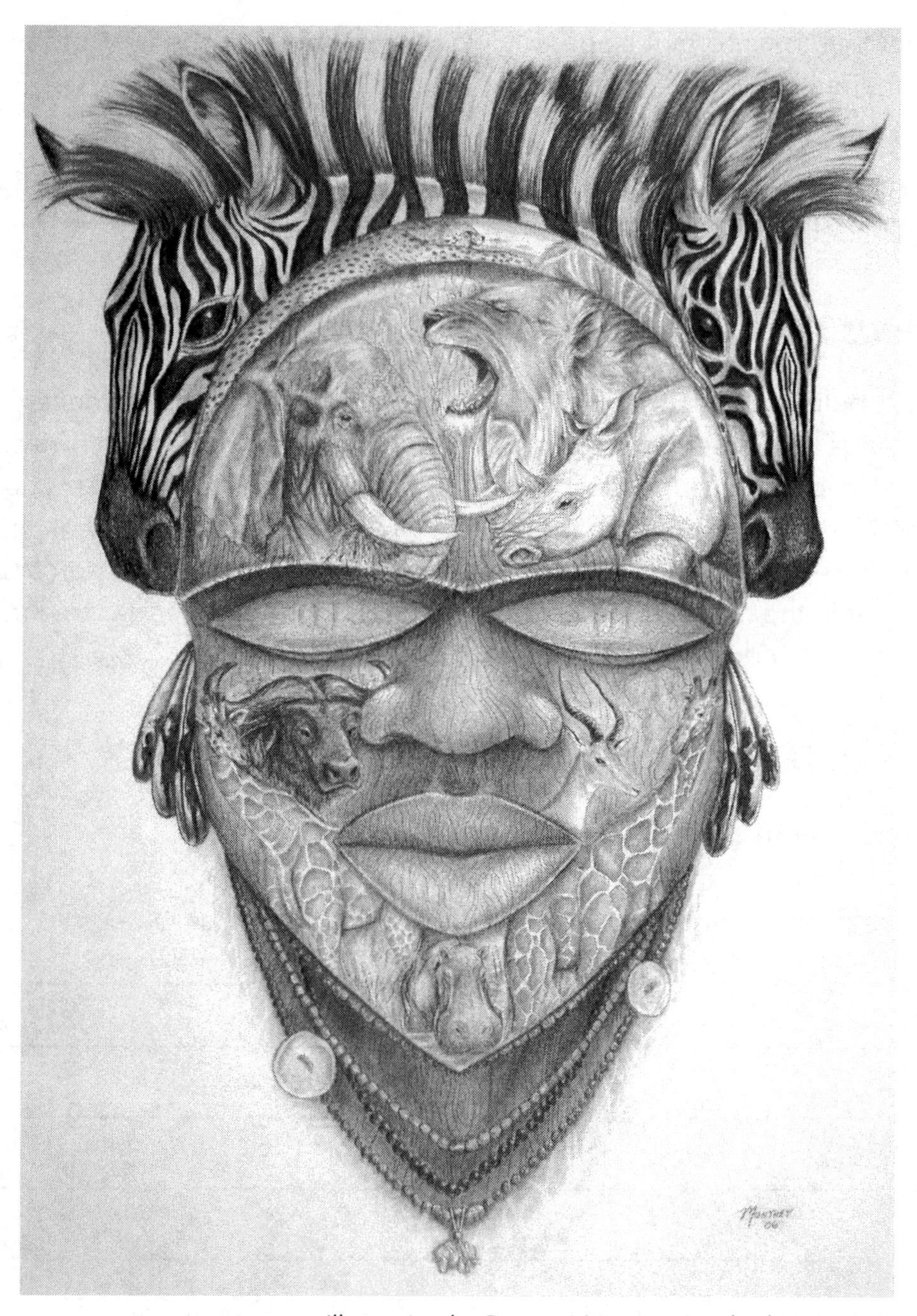

Illustration by Duane Montney, *Masked Menagerie*

- *Denial*: This occurs when a woman refuses to recognize the problem. There is a tendency to say that the abuse was not a big deal or deny that the abuse is occurring. The woman may make excuses or rationalize the behavior.
- *Self-blame*: The woman now recognizes there is a problem, but she blames herself. She may feel she "deserves" to be beaten. She believes it is her fault that her abuser is upset and violent. She thinks that if only she behaved better everything would be fine.

- *Insight*: In this important stage, the woman realizes that she is not to blame and sees the reality of her situation.
- *Resolution*: With insight and adequate support, the woman is now able to make and act on effective plans to protect herself and remove herself from the abusive situation. She is ready to move on with her life.

What about Treatment for Male Batterers?

Some women believe that if only their partner would get domestic-violence-offender treatment, things would get better. While getting such treatment is clearly a step in the right direction, recent research has shown that it has little effect on preventing future abuse. Overall, men who complete treatment still have about a 60 percent chance of being violent in the future. Men who do not have treatment have a 65 percent chance of being violent in the future. In other words, do not count on offender treatment as a satisfactory answer to domestic violence.

Exercise 5-5: Domestic Violence

Directions: Read each question carefully and write down your best answer.

1. What are some of the main reason that women do not leave abusive relationships? Which of these reasons would affect you the most?

   ____

   ____

   ____

   ____

2. If your partner abuses you, then starts to apologize and promises never to do it again, where are you in the cycle of violence? What should you expect to happen next?

   ____

   ____

   ____

   ____

3. What is the most important thing for a survivor of domestic violence to do?

____

____

____

____

4. Why do abusers often prevent women from having anything to do with their friends or families?

____

____

____

____

5. If your partner completes a domestic-violence-treatment program, what can you realistically expect to happen?

____

____

____

____

Lesson 5-6: Gender Issues and Mothering

Raising Your Son

Sons at Risk

Overall, boys are at much greater risk for getting in trouble than girls are. Boys commit the majority of antisocial acts in school. Compared to girls, they are twice as likely to have learning problems and ten times more likely to have attention difficulties. Boys make up two-thirds of all special education classes. They are also much more likely to get into trouble with the law and to commit violent crimes. Boys also have higher suicide rates. When we neglect boys, we are in for trouble. While there are many factors to consider, boys with no father or a troubled father are much more likely to experience all of these problems. Boys with both mothers and fathers who are committed to them generally do much better in life.

Mothers and Sons

Mothers and sons can often be quite close. This is especially true during the early years, before adolescence, when the need to be independent starts to pull them away. Most successful men have had mothers who were supportive and nurturing. Your relationship with your son is also very important since it will help determine how he relates to other women in the future. For this reason, you should make an effort to teach your son to show respect for you and other women.

Boys often seem embarrassed by displays of affection from their mothers. However, make a point to hug them or kiss them on the cheek when you get a chance. Although he may act uncomfortable, such physical contact binds him to you in a powerful unspoken way.

Sons also need positive male role models. If your son's father is not available to fill this role, you should seek out other possibilities. You might consider some male relative, a scouting or youth leader, a teacher, or a volunteer through organizations such as a Big Brothers Big Sisters of America.

A Method to Talk to Your Son

Many boys have difficulty opening up and talking about their feelings. One method to improve communication with your son involves finding a safe place where your son feels that no one will make fun of him. Next, find an activity he enjoys (a game or a sports activity). While playing, you can ask questions to draw your son out and see how he is feeling. You could start with something like, "You seemed really quiet after basketball practice yesterday. Is everything going okay? How are you feeling?" Many counselors often talk to children while playing checkers or shooting baskets. (Do not get too involved in the competition, it can spoil everything.) You may be surprised how your son can open up during these talks. You can use this time to talk about some of your own struggles when you were younger. This can help your son see that it is possible to work through these things.

Raising Your Daughter

Like Mother Like Daughter: Being a Good Example

Most of us would like our daughters to be like us, but without our faults. Women do not enjoy seeing their own faults in their daughters. Some mothers tend to punish their daughters too severely for these faults. Make no mistake about it, if you have a daughter, you will become her role model. This means she will learn about what it means to be a woman and mother by watching what you do. This is a huge responsibility. She will learn from you how to treat other people. She will learn what the important things in life are. She also will learn how to handle things when the going gets tough.

Girls who grow up with mothers who control themselves learn how to control their own emotions. This is also true of decision-making and intolerance for disrespect. In a home where the mother expresses her feelings and thoughts and stands up for her point of view, daughters learn the importance of asserting themselves. Mothers who will not put up with anyone making fun of them or physically harming them teach their daughters that they also have the right to be respected.

Girls model themselves after the women in their lives. They imitate them and look to them as sources for their identity and self-esteem. Now is the time to fearlessly look at your own behavior and make any needed changes. One of the best things you can do for your daughter is to work out your own issues. For example, if substance abuse or being too dependent is a problem for you, getting help is critical. You need to get help not only for yourself, but also for the sake of your daughter. Again, look at your behavior.

Raising Your Daughter: Some Guidelines

Listed below are several suggestions about raising a daughter in today's world. Today's environment can be a dangerous and unfriendly place for girls. Often, they are discouraged from having high goals. Others may use them or overprotect them. Your goal is to have a daughter who is self-sufficient, independent, and has the self-esteem necessary to make good judgments. These are some suggestions to help:

- **Encourage your daughter to participate in sports and physical activities.** Teach her to play catch, tag, jump rope, basketball, hockey, or soccer. Girls who are physically active are less likely to get pregnant, drop out of school, or tolerate abuse. Girls who are the most physically active have mothers who actively participate with them.
- **Work toward making the world a better place for girls.** The world today holds many dangers for our daughters. Work with other mothers to end violence against females. Oppose the exploitation of women and the idea that "boys are always better than girls." Encourage your daughter to prove stereotypes wrong. Let her know that girls can succeed in sports, math, science, and politics just as well as boys. Encourage her to explore all options regarding her future occupation.
- **Teach your daughter how to manage money and pay bills.** This is an important skill that girls often are not taught.
- **Do not make physical appearance most important.** Girls are at a very high risk to develop eating disorders. Make sure you daughter eats a healthy diet, avoids most junk foods, and gets plenty of physical activity. Do not encourage fad or crash diets. Do not permit name-calling or allow others to tease her about her weight or appearance.
- **Keep your daughter out of the middle of conflicts between you and her father.** Do not seek your daughter's support when you have arguments with her father, and do not use her to carry messages between the two of you.
- **Give your daughter consistent time and attention.** Give this attention in person, on the phone, and by sending mail. Set aside some time each day to talk to her about her concerns.
- **Focus on positive aspects of your daughter's behavior.** It is easy to spot mistakes and point out things that need to be changed. Encourage positive habits rather than constantly describing problems. Look for things to praise.
- **Know what you daughter is doing.** Be active in her projects and activities. Know who her friends are, what activities she is interested in, and what she likes to do.
- **Get involved with your daughter.** For example, for many years the Girl Scouts of the USA have operated a program called Girl Scouts Beyond Bars in partnership with the National Institute of Justice. Girls visit their incarcerated mothers weekly to monthly to take part in mother/daughter Girl Scout troop

meetings. Check with your facility to see if a similar program is available (www.girlscouts.org/program/program_opportunities/community/gsbb.asp).

- **Most importantly, listen to your daughter.** Do not always lecture or argue. Engage in conversations. Build a bond that will be important when your daughter really needs to listen to you. Use active listening and serve as a sounding board for your daughter's concerns. Do not immediately rush into a "fixing mode." Allow her to identify her own answers and solutions. This is difficult for many mothers who always want to help and make things easier for their daughters. It is important that she learn how to solve problems herself. This is the way she will become independent and self-sufficient.

Things You Should Know

Having a daughter requires a lot of time and attention. As the mother of a girl, you need to know your daughter. Below are some things that every mother should know about her daughter as she grows up.

- Who are her three best friends?
- What are her goals?
- How does she feel about her looks?
- What are her favorite school subjects?
- What school project is she working on?
- Does she have the same freedom as her brother?
- Does she know stories about you when you were growing up?
- Does she really know that you love and approve of her?

By knowing these things, you are in a position to have a solid relationship with your daughter. This relationship can be a great source of comfort and security to her and satisfaction to you.

Cultural Attitudes and Gender Differences

Some mothers are much more strict about adolescent girls' behavior than they are about adolescent boys' behavior. They may be more permissive with boys, allowing them more independence and opportunities for sexual exploration. Girls, on the other hand, are expected to refrain from all such activities and are often given very little freedom. Some of these differences are rooted in cultural beliefs about the importance of manliness in boys and purity in girls. While you should respect cultural traditions, mothers also need to examine their own personal beliefs to make sure they are being fair to both sons and daughters.

When There Are Two Mothers

Lesbian Parents

Over the past thirty years, lesbian couples raising children have become increasingly more commonplace. Many lesbian mothers may have special concerns about parenting and their children's welfare.

Among the most common issues are thing such as:

- **Fears their children will have problems:** Current research shows that when all other things are equal, children raised in lesbian families do as well as other children. Their mental health, school performance, and self-esteem are the same as that of other children
- **Worries about their children's gender/sexual preference issues:** Studies also show that living in a lesbian family does not damage or distort children's sexual choice. As they grow older, their sexual behaviors and preferences are the same as other children's.
- **Worries that the family lacks appropriate role models:** Some lesbian mothers worry that the lack of a male role model in the immediate family will harm boys as they grow up. This is not the case. Studies show that children in lesbian families tend to have even more contact with grandparents and extended family members than most other children. In addition to the extended family and friends, scouting, church activities, and programs such as Big Brothers Big Sisters can help provide additional appropriate male models for boys and female models for girls.
- **How to best share work and parenting responsibilities:** Research shows that most lesbian couples are able to develop a practical division of the work and parenting responsibilities. It is important that this division be fair. It should not place either partner in the role of the "bad guy," the one who dishes out all the punishment.
- **Dealing with discrimination:** Of all the issues, this one may be the most troublesome for lesbian families. Strong evidence shows that children in lesbian families tend to be as happy as other children are. However, they may be more aware of stress and disapproval from outside the family than other children are. Mothers should teach children how to deal with others who may not approve of their family's lifestyle. Some practical tips include:

— Understand your children's level of development. Make sure they are capable of understanding whatever you are trying to teach them.
— Be sensitive to their feelings and talk openly and honestly.
— As needed, talk to other adults who may be responsible for situations where negative comments or treatment takes place (teachers, youth leaders, neighbors, and so forth).
— Do not let your children deal with discrimination alone. Support them.
— Do not gloss over minor teasing or put-downs. It only gets worse. You do not want your children to blame themselves.
— Find other families like yours that you can use for support.
— Avoid forcing your children to choose between themselves and the family.
— Be positive about your personal and family identity, and set a good example.
— Send the message, "You can handle it" in strong and clear terms.
— For teasing, you also can teach them to do the following things:
  - Say some positive things to themselves
  - Not give the teaser attention by getting upset or hurt
  - Imagine the hurtful words bouncing off them
  - Confront the teasing and assertively ask the other person to stop
  - Respond to the teasing with the phrase, "So what?"
  - Ask for help from a responsible adult

Exercise 5-6: Gender Issues and Mothering

Directions: Read each question carefully and write down your best answer.

1. What are some ways that you can show affection to your son? List and describe at least three different ways.

____

____

____

____

2. Do you think girls and boys should have the same rules? This includes things such as curfews, going out alone, having a car, and dating. Explain your answer.

____

____

____

____

3. What do sons need from mothers? List at least three things.

____

____

____

____

4. List three reasons why girls need to have a mother in their life. What sort of things can a girl learn from her mother?

____

____

____

____

5. If your daughter is upset and having a problem with other kids at school, what are some things you could do to help?

____

____

____

____

6. How can you let your sons and daughters know that despite making mistakes, you still are proud of them? List and explain at least three ways.

7. What are some benefits of physical activity for girls? What is the most important thing that encourages girls to be physically active?

8. Some mothers act as if they are playmates for their children. Other mothers are very strict and only punish their children. What role do you think a mother should take with her kids?

9. Some mothers tell their children, "Do what I say, not what I do." Does this work? What influences children the most—your words or your behavior?

10. What are three things a mother should know about her daughter?

____

____

____

____

Chapter 6

Developing Your Personal Parenting and Reunification Plan

This chapter offers you a chance to use the information in the previous chapters and lessons. You will write your personal parenting and reunification plan. You can use this plan as a guide for your future relationship with your children.

The first lesson in this chapter discusses the importance of preparing yourself to handle the stress of caring for your children. We describe ways to handle stress and make good plans. Developing your own personal stress-management plan is the goal of this lesson.

The second lesson helps you identify several things you can begin doing right now to help prepare for having your family back together again. Even if reunification is far away, there is plenty for you to start working on now.

The final lesson challenges you to put all your mothering knowledge and skills to work to create your own personal plan for parenting and reunification.

Lesson 6-1: Your Own Stress-Management Plan

What is Stress?

If you are managing the stress of being incarcerated, you already know you can handle anything. The stress of being a mother is not as strong as incarceration. Nevertheless, it is important to know how you can handle it. What is stress? *Stress* is your body's reaction to pressure, tension, and demands for change. S*tressors* are things that cause pressure.

The demands of raising children are constant. They never let up. Furthermore, the stakes are very high. The job you do may determine your child's future happiness. This is not a job for the weak or cowardly. However, stress can affect even the strongest person. Stress wears down the body's ability to cope. Stress affects not only your feelings and thinking, but also your health. Small amounts of stress can help motivate you to get things done. Excessive stress is very destructive.

Effect of Stress on Mothers

What happens when stress begins to wear you down? Unless there is some major bad event, stress increases gradually. You may not even know it at first. There are dozens of symptoms of stress. Some of these can hurt your ability to be an effective mother. Among the most destructive stress symptoms are the following:

- Being impatient with your children
- Feeling annoyed
- Losing your temper
- Screaming at family members
- Hitting or abusing your children
- Ignoring family members or wanting to be alone
- Abusing alcohol or drugs
- Feeling sick

Effect of the Mother's Stress on Children

Having a stressed-out mother puts children at greater risk of becoming stressed, too. Children may copy stressed behavior and show stress symptoms themselves. In some cases, the child may try to take on the responsibilities of the mother. Children may do chores, try to earn money, worry about bills, or take care of brothers and sisters. They do this to try to help the mother.

Some children may think their "bad behavior" is to blame for their mother's stress. These children may work very hard to be perfect. They believe that if they are perfect, the mother will not have problems. This puts too much pressure on the child.

Symptoms and Signs of Stress

Stress can show itself in a variety of ways. The list on page 202 shows only a small number of the many different forms of stress symptoms.

Types of Stress

Parenting stress comes in several different forms. There are four general categories of stress:

1. **Survival stress** occurs when something threatens your life or health. During survival stress, your body prepares itself to fight or run away. To do this, your body goes on high alert, which takes a great deal of energy.
2. **Financial and job stress** stem from worries about finances and bills and pressures from work or trying to find and maintain a job.
3. **Environmental stress** comes from the stressors in your surroundings. Stressors may include noise, crowding, pollution, uneven temperatures, clutter, or other things that wear you out or annoy you. This also includes interpersonal stress such as living in a place where you are constantly belittled, criticized, or disrespected.
4. **Overwork stress** builds up over time when you are trying to do too much. You feel frustrated and the situation seems impossible. This sort of stress gets worse when you are under time pressure. This type of stress leads to chronic tiredness.

Managing Your Stress

There are seven key elements in any effective stress-management program:

1. **Constructive self-talk:** This is first because of its importance. To a large degree, emotional stress stems from the things that we tell ourselves. By making demands and criticizing ourselves, we increase the amount of stress we have. By thinking that disappointing situations are the end of the world, we make ourselves feel even worse. Increasing healthy self-talk is a good way to reduce

Common Signs and Symptoms of Stress

Physical Symptoms: Feeling tired all the time; feeling nauseous; fainting; vomiting; being dizzy; having weakness; experiencing chest pain or back pain; having high cholesterol, headaches, high blood pressure, a rapid pulse, or tremors; grinding your teeth; increased sweating; problems breathing; sleeping too much or not being able to fall asleep.

Cognitive Symptoms: Going over and over the same thoughts in your head; confusion; nightmares; suspicion; negative thoughts you cannot get rid of; increased blame; poor problem-solving; difficulty concentrating; memory problems; disorientation; decreased alertness; increase in careless errors; feeling out of it, or always feeling on guard; having attention problems; or racing thoughts.

Emotional Symptoms: Fear, guilt, grief, panic, denial, anxiety, jumpiness, irritability, depression, anger, emotional outbursts, and feeling overwhelmed.

Behavioral Symptoms: Going off by yourself, lying, stealing, breaking rules, having an inability to rest, pacing, using jerky movements, staying away from friends, talking more or less, having a change in appetite and eating, or increasing alcohol or substance use.

stress. We should encourage ourselves as we would friends. (Recall Lesson 1-2 on the importance of self-talk. You may want to review this.)

2. **Physical activity:** Exercise and physical activity are great treatments for stress. Such activities allow your body to work off stress in a positive way.
3. **Adequate Support:** People under stress need help. A strong support network of family and friends can make a big difference. Besides emotional support, they can help with many of the problems that people face. Providing babysitting, transportation, money, and help in day-to-day activities can significantly reduce stress from overwork. It is good to build strong ties and let others help you. Members of twelve-step groups also can be part of your support system.
4. **Relaxation Skills:** People under stress need to learn how to relax. Learning to teach your body to rest is very important. Consider learning how to meditate or how to use deep muscle relaxation, or maybe soak in a hot bathtub.

5. **Good Nutrition:** Good nutrition plays an important role in stress-management. The use of alcohol, nicotine, caffeine, sugar, and excessive junk food can make the stress in your life even worse. Focus on keeping a healthy diet. Emphasize whole grains, fruits and vegetables, fish, lean meats, and nuts. Limit junk foods and treats. Keep yourself fit and strong, as if you are running a race.
6. **Adequate Rest and Recreation:** It is important that you get adequate rest and sleep. Even with a busy schedule and a million things to do, do not let yourself get exhausted and run down. Also, make sure that you set aside time to have fun. Laughter, companionship, and closeness with others are important parts of a good stress-management program.
7. **Life-Management Skills:** You often can reduce stress if you know ways to manage the demands you face. Good time management, child management, and anger management skills can go a long way in reducing your level of stress.

Time Management

Using your time well is an essential life-management skill. There are so many things to do each day. Having children creates an enormous number of additional demands. Since there is so little time for all the jobs you do, you must learn to manage your time. Good time management can help you reduce your stress levels significantly. Below are some of the keys to effective time management. Read them carefully and see which ones you might be able to use.

1. **Set Priorities:** It is best to spend your limited time on the most important things. Therefore, you must decide what is most important and what can wait a little. This usually means making a list and focusing your attention only on the things that make it to the top.
2. **Learn to Say "No":** Since your time is limited, you need to learn to refuse jobs that are not important. This can be hard for some people. Do not automatically say "yes" every time someone asks you to do something. Many of these things are not at the top of your list. Before saying "yes," tell the other person you will need to think it over.
3. **Make a Schedule:** Listing the things you want to do will help you work on the most important things first. Once you make a schedule, follow it.
4. **Know How Long Things Really Take:** Many people are unrealistic in guessing how long things take. These people are always late or in a rush. They seem to think they can do things much faster than they actually can. Give yourself extra time so that you are not always falling behind schedule.

5. **Do Not Be a Perfectionist:** Only insist on perfection for the most important things, such as your child's health and safety. Many people waste much time trying to make things that are already good "perfect." This extra effort can cost a great deal of time.
6. **Schedule Fun Things:** When you make your schedule, include enjoyable, relaxing, and fun activities. These scheduled activities are great stress reducers.
7. **Be Organized:** People waste a lot of time because they are not organized. Clutter can cost you time. You can never find things. Invest in things that help you stay organized such as bins or baskets or a special place to keep your keys and wallet. Computers and electronic organizers can help you stay organized. Learn to throw away things when you no longer need them.
8. **Give Some Jobs to Other People:** Learn to share responsibilities with others. There may be many jobs that you can hand over to other family members, including your children. Some people have to do everything themselves because they want it done in a specific way.
9. **Get Some Help:** People feel stressed out because they do not have enough help. Family and friends might be willing to help you from time to time. Neighbors, people from church, and work acquaintances all may be willing to pitch in and help you at different times. Get as much help as you can. Do not be embarrassed to ask for help, but you do not want to use and abuse others. Be quick to offer to return a favor.
10. **Trade Time for Money:** Sometimes we take on jobs that we should hire someone else to do. Always consider the cost of your own time when figuring out how best to do a job. Sometimes a professional can do it easier, quicker, and cheaper than you can.
11. **Get a Really Good Day Care Program:** Take the time to find the best day care program you can. This will pay off in the future. A good day care program can save you a lot of time and help you out in a pinch.
12. **Find a Quiet Space:** Try to find a quiet space within your home. You may need to set a certain area as off-limits to kids. This is a place where you can work without interruption and really get things done.
13. **Break Big Jobs into Small Steps:** Often times we put off very large tasks until they become a major source of stress. By breaking big jobs into very small steps, you can work on them effectively.

14. **Combine Jobs:** Learn to multitask. This means doing more than one thing at a time. Some people catch up on their reading while exercising. Others fold the laundry while checking the weather on television. Another way of saving time is to combine errands when you leave the house. Plan the most efficient route to save you time and to keep you from backtracking.

15. **Do Not Waste Waiting Time:** If you are going somewhere where you will have to wait (such as the doctor's office or the department of motor vehicles), take along other work or jobs to do while you wait.

Exercise 6-1: Designing Your Stress-Management Plan

Part I: Constructive Self-Talk

Write down three other positive statements that you can say to yourself when you begin to feel stress from trying to raise your kids:

1. I do not have to be perfect in everything I do.

2. If I do not get everything done, that is okay.

3. ____

____

____

____

4. ____

____

____

____

5. ____

____

____

____

Part II: Physical Activity

Circle those physical activities that you will try to do every week.

Running	Jogging	Walking	Bicycling	Skating
Basketball	Swimming	Weights	Riding a Stationary Bike	

Other: ____

Where will you do it? ____

When will you do it (days and hours)? ____

Part III: Finding Adequate Support

1. List family members and friends who might be willing to help you:

____

____

____

____

2. Where else will you look to get help and support? Consider twelve-step groups, religious groups, neighbors, people at work, in-laws, acquaintances, or parents of your children's friends.

____

____

____

____

4. In an emergency, who could help watch your kids?

____

____

____

____

5. Who could you get to babysit for your kids when you need to go out?

____

____

____

____

6. What other parents would you be willing to help?

____

____

____

____

The Ten-Step Stress Relief Method

1. Sit down in a comfortable chair.
2. Describe what is annoying you.
3. Say to yourself, "I do not have to feel upset about this."
4. Take two deep breaths, and slowly exhale.
5. Identify the tensest part of your body and try to smooth out those muscles.
6. Imagine that you are wearing a very heavy coat that presses down on your shoulders.
7. Move your head slowly in a circular motion twice in both directions.
8. Recall a pleasant thought or memory. Try to remember the feelings, the sights, the sounds, and even the smells that went with it. Think about it for fifteen to twenty seconds.
9. Take two more deep breaths, and slowly exhale.
10. Say to yourself, "I will handle this."

Part IV: Using Relaxation Skills

1. List three positive things you could do to unwind and relax if you are feeling upset about your kids (no alcohol or drugs).

   ____

   ____

   ____

   ____

2. Read the ten-step stress relief method on the prior page. What pleasant thought or memory could you use in step eight?

   ____

   ____

   ____

   ____

Part V: Good Nutrition

Indicate which of these foods you should increase or decrease. Circle the best answer.

1.	**Example:** Green leafy vegetables	(More)	Less
2.	Snack cakes	More	Less
3.	Beer	More	Less
4.	Fruits	More	Less
5.	Whole grain breads and cereal	More	Less
6.	Orange and yellow vegetables	More	Less
7.	Fast food burgers	More	Less
8.	Fish	More	Less
9.	Lean chicken	More	Less

10. Potato chips — More Less
11. Doughnuts — More Less
12. Chocolate — More Less
13. Nuts — More Less
14. Vitamins — More Less
15. Bologna sandwiches — More Less

Part VI: Life-Management Skills

1. List the following tasks in priority order. Put the most important job first and the least important job last.
   A. Pick up clothes at cleaner
   B. Take daughter to doctor to get her immunizations
   C. Buy food for tonight's dinner
   D. Buy beer and cigarettes for your boyfriend

   ____

   ____

   ____

   ____

2. It is time to get the annual registration for your car. In your state, you must have proof of insurance. Your car also must pass a vehicle inspection. It also must have a separate special emission-control inspection. Break this big job into four smaller steps and list them below.

   ____

   ____

   ____

   ____

3. Every time you have to take your kids somewhere, they can never find their shoes. This always makes you late. What are some things you could do to make sure that the kids will always have their shoes ready when it is time to go?

____

____

____

____

4. It is a Saturday and you have many things to do. You need to take the kids to a party, cut the grass, and go shopping. Before you do these things, you look down and see that the kitchen floor needs cleaning. You sweep the floor and it looks okay, but you start thinking maybe you should mop and polish it. If you do, you will never get all the other things done. What are some things you can tell yourself about the floor that can help you get on with your tasks?

____

____

____

____

5. Your son is now fourteen years old. List three household chores that you could give him to do. Also list three jobs that you should not allow him to do.

____

____

____

____

Lesson 6-2: Things You Can Do Right Now

Getting a Good Start

By using this workbook, you have already taken the first steps to prepare for reunification with your children. You may also have done other things to prepare the way. Look at the list below. These are several things you can do now to work toward successful reunification. Not all of these things are possible since different facilities have different policies and programs available.

You want to make good use of your time. Working on these tasks will help structure your day. It also will demonstrate to others your commitment to taking responsibility for your children. Check the box next to the items that you already have done, or plan to do.

Things You Can Do Now to Prepare for Reunification

1. ❑ Ask your chaplain, counselor, or other facility staff member about your facility's policies regarding child visitation, letters, telephone calls, and sending audio tapes.
2. ❑ Try to establish some type of regular visitation with your children.
3. ❑ If you are permitted to make audio tapes, use these to tell or read stories and share thoughts and memories with your children. They can listen to these tapes when they miss you.
4. ❑ Plan how often you will contact your child. This includes phone calls, tape recordings, visits, and writing letters. Keep your promises about making contact.
5. ❑ Remember family birthdays, holidays, and special events with cards, letters, or phone calls. If you can make crafts, make small gifts, pictures, or coloring books to send. If possible, purchase small items for your children from the commissary or mail order catalogs.
6. ❑ Clear up any other pending legal problems that could be a problem at reunification such as parking tickets, credit problems, and so on. Consider credit counseling if this is a problem.
7. ❑ Take as many self-improvement classes as you can, such as financial management, GED or college courses, anger management, addiction/relapse prevention, education, relationships and communication courses,

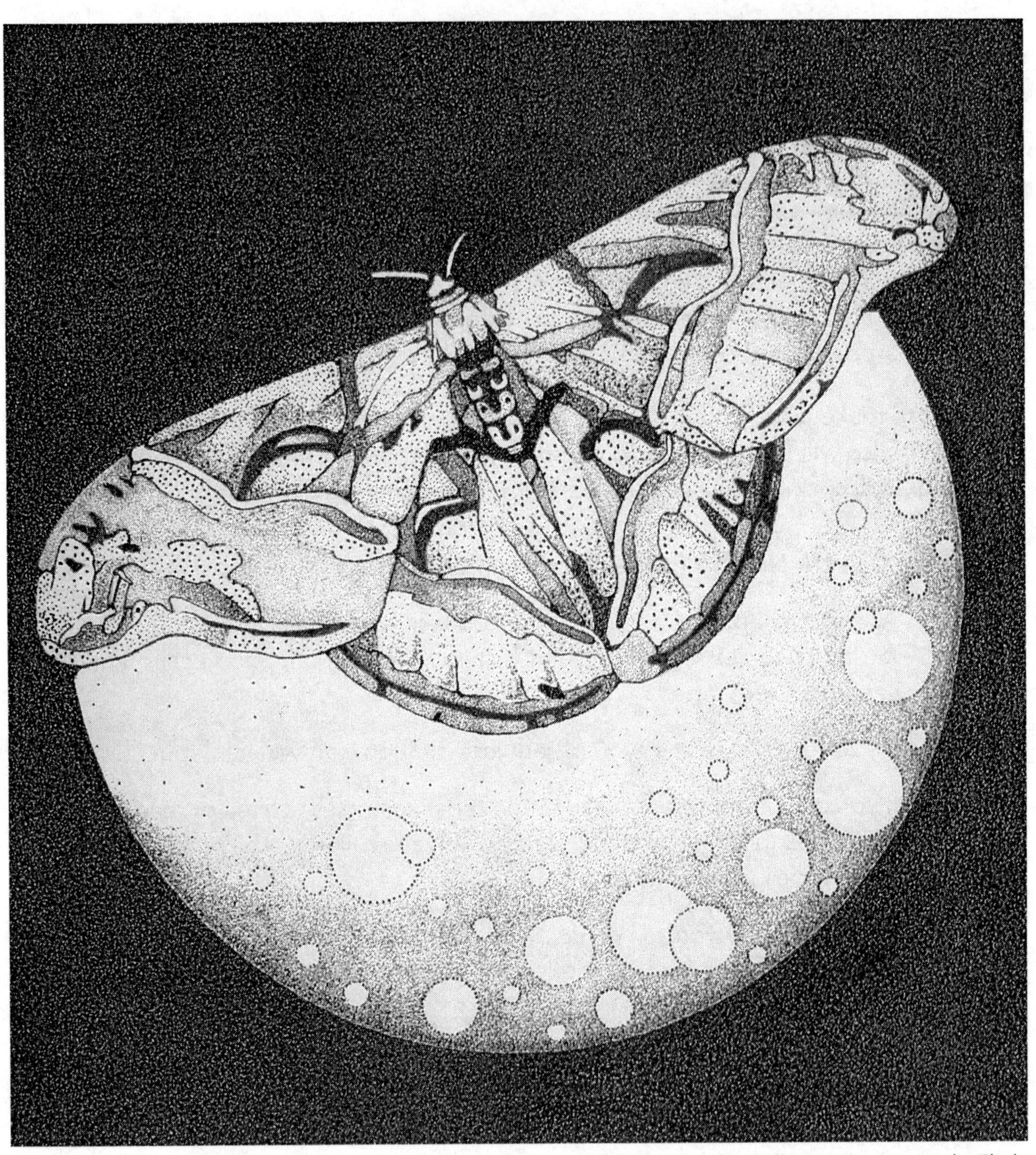

Illustration by William Kissane, *Night Flight*

and job skills training. Also, use the library to learn all you can to be a better mom. Some suggested references on parenting are at the end of this book.

8. ❑ Learn about available programs that could help you reach your goals once you are released. Seek out programs and counseling about housing, jobs, legal problems, credit problems, substance abuse, and mental health counseling.

9. ❑ If you have conflicts with your children's current caretakers, work on making an ally out of them. Find ways to work with them in a respectful manner. Apologize. Open up lines of communication with them to plan for the future. You need their cooperation.

10. ❑ To improve relationships with other family members, start writing letters or making phone calls to reestablish contact. Consider making amends and apologizing to any people you have hurt. If people have said hurtful things to you, decide if you can forgive them.

11. ❑ Seek regular guidance and counseling from appropriate staff (psychologists, chaplains, case managers, correctional counselors).

12. ❑ Complete your comprehensive reunification plan (Lesson 6-3).

Do not worry if there are things that you cannot do now. Focus all your attention on the ones that you can.

Exercise 6-2: Preparing for Unification

Directions: Read each question carefully and write in your best response.

1. Describe the visits or other contact you have with your children right now.

____

____

____

____

2. What could you do to increase or improve your contact with your children?

____

____

____

____

3. What sort of relations do you have with the father (or fathers) of your children now?

____

____

____

____

4. What can you do to strengthen or improve this (these) relationship(s)?

____

____

____

____

5. What self-improvement classes have you taken, and which ones will you try to take?

____

____

____

____

6. Do you have any legal issues that you need to take care of before reunification, such as parking tickets or pending charges?

____

____

____

____

7. What can you do to start working on the legal issues listed in question number six?

____

____

____

____

8. Who can you talk to about the things you need to do for reunification?

____

____

____

____

9. How would you describe your relationships with other family members? Is there anything you can do to improve these relationships?

____

____

____

____

10. What do you think will be the most difficult thing you have to do to get back with your kids?

____

____

____

____

Lesson 6-3: Completing Your Parenting and Reunification Plan

Using What You Have Learned

This final lesson is devoted entirely to making your own personal parenting plan. This plan may take a while to complete. You should try to make it as detailed as possible. You may need to think about some items for a while. For other issues, you may not know your answer(s) yet. It may be helpful to share your answers with others so that you can see what other possibilities exist. However, do not just copy a plan from someone else. You must personalize this plan. It has to work for you.

Illustration by Mike Routley, *The Long March*

My Personal Parenting and Reunification Plan

1. Your Name: ______________________________ Plan Date: __________________

2. Anticipated Date of Reunification: ______________________________________

3. List Your Children:

	Child's Name	Gender	Child's Current Age	Child's Age at Reunification
a.	______________________________	_________	___________	______________
b.	______________________________	_________	___________	______________
c.	______________________________	_________	___________	______________
d.	______________________________	_________	___________	______________
e.	______________________________	_________	___________	______________
f.	______________________________	_________	___________	______________
g.	______________________________	_________	___________	______________
h.	______________________________	_________	___________	______________
i.	______________________________	_________	___________	______________

4. What specific things can you do right now to prepare your family and children for reunification?

____

____

____

____

5. Where will you live? Can anyone help you get on your feet?

____

____

____

____

6. Where will your children live? Do you have a temporary and a long-term plan?

____

____

____

____

7. If you do not have custody of your children, what sort of visitation (how often, how long) will you try to arrange?

____

____

____

____

8. How will you support your children financially? What job will you try to get? How will you try to get it?

____

____

____

____

9. Who will take care of your children while you are at work?

10. What positive discipline methods will you use with your children at the time of unification? Are these the right methods for how old the children will be at that time?

11. What will your relationship with the children's father(s) be like? How can you make this as positive as possible for the children?

12. What other relatives will be involved with you and your children, and how will you get along with them?

13. What will you tell your children about your experiences in prison or jail when they ask you?

____

____

____

____

14. What holidays and events are special and important to your family?

____

____

____

____

15. What family and cultural traditions are important enough to you so that you want to teach your children about them (ceremonies, values, activities)?

____

____

____

____

16. How will you get dental and medical health care for your children?

____

____

____

____

17. Do your children have any special health care needs such as a special diet or need for regular treatments? How will you make sure these needs are met?

18. What happens if there is an emergency? Who can help you?

19. What are some places, organizations, or agencies you plan to contact for help (housing, health care, jobs, medical care, and legal help)?

20. What important beliefs or values do you want your children to learn?

21. What do you plan to do to encourage your children's spiritual development? Will they attend religious services? What kind, and where?

____

____

____

____

22. In what grades in school will your children be? Where will they attend school (include preschool or day care)?

____

____

____

____

23. What plans will you make for higher education for your kids (saving for college, trade school, or other)?

____

____

____

____

24. What things will you do to help your children succeed in school?

____

____

____

____

25. What things can you do to better manage your own stress?

____

____

____

____

26. What will you do when you need a break from your children?

____

____

____

____

27. In regard to your children, what do you think will be the most difficult things for you to do? How will you approach this difficulty?

____

____

____

____

28. What will you do to protect your children from the dangers of gang participation?

____

____

____

____

29. Explain why you want to be reunified with your kids. What are your reasons?

____

____

____

____

Congratulations and Good Luck!

Sources of Information

In preparing for reunification with your children, you will need a lot of information. There are three main sources of information available:

- **People:** Ask your corrections counselor, probation officer, chaplain, attorney, advocate, family, friends, or any one else to get you information about jobs and work, child support, financial planning, and other services you might need such as counseling or substance abuse treatment.
- **Publications:** Check the library for publications and references. Write to the federal government for information; they have many free publications. Bookstores are also good sources of information.
- **The Internet:** Most correctional facilities do not allow inmates Internet access. Ask others to check for you. When you are released, check out the public library for Internet access. Many web sites and search engines can link you to great information on parenting, jobs, and many other topics.

Listed below are some suggested sources of information.

Supplemental Readings and Resources for Incarcerated Mothers

Allen, K. E. and L. R. Marotz. 2000. *By the Ages: Behavior and Development of Children Prebirth through Eight.* Albany, New York: Thomson Learning, Delmar.

Bass, E. and L. Davis. 1994. *The Courage to Heal: A Guide for Women Survivors of Child Sexual Abuse, 3rd Edition.* New York: Harper & Row.

Berk, L. E. 2006. *Child Development*, 7th ed. Boston: Allyn & Bacon.

Gordon, T. 2000. *Parent Effectiveness Training.* New York: Three Rivers Press.

Haines, S. 1999. *The Survivors Guide to Sex: How to Have a Great Sex Life—Even if You've Been Sexually Abused.* San Francisco: Cleis Press, Inc.

Mayes, L. C. and D. J. Cohen. 2002. *The Yale Child Study Center Guide to Understanding Your Child.* Boston: Little Brown & Co.

Pruitt, D. B., ed. 1998. American Academy of Child and Adolescent Psychiatry. *Your Child: Emotional, Behavioral, and Cognitive Development from Birth through Preadolescence.* New York: HarperCollins.

Urquhart, J. and M. C. Cullen. 2004. *Cage Your Rage For Women.* Alexandria, Virginia: American Correctional Association.

Welo, B. K. 2005. *Picking Up the Pieces: A Workbook for Incarcerated Women.* Alexandria, Virginia: American Correctional Association.

Groups that Can Provide Information or Help for Incarcerated Mothers

(For many of these numbers you must leave a message. If possible, check out the web sites first.)

Aid to Children of Imprisoned Mothers
906 Ralph David Abernathy Blvd. SW
Atlanta, GA 30310
(404) 755-3262; Fax (404) 755-3294
www.takingaim.net

Alcoholic Anonymous
Grand Central Station
P.O. Box 459
New York, NY 10163
www.alcoholics-anonymous.org

Center for Children with Incarcerated Parents
P.O. Box 41-286
Eagle Rock, CA 90041
(626) 449-2470; Fax (626) 449-9001
www.e-ccip.org

Center for Family Policy and Practice
23 N. Pinckney St, Ste 210
Madison, WI 53703
(608) 257-3148; Fax (608) 257-4686
http://www.cffpp.org

Chicago Legal Advocacy for Incarcerated Mothers (CLAIM)
220 S State St., Ste 830
Chicago, IL 60604
(312) 675-0911; Fax (312) 332-2570
www.claim-il.org

CURE (Citizens United for Rehabilitation of Errants)
P.O. Box 2310, National Capitol Station
Washington, DC 20013
(202) 789-2126
www.curenational.org

Family and Corrections Network
32 Oak Grove Rd
Palmyra, VA 22963
(434) 589-3036; Fax (434) 589-6520
www.fcnetwork.org
This organization does not mail out information. You must download all educational materials from the Internet.

Family Support America
205 W. Randolph St., Ste 2222
Chicago, IL 60606
(312) 338-0900; Fax (312) 338-1522
www.frca.org

Families With a Future
100 McAllister St.
San Francisco, CA 94102
(415) 255-7036 ext. 320; Fax (415) 552-3150

Federal Resource Center for Children of Prisoners
440 First St., NW, Third Floor
Washington, DC 20001
(202) 638-2952; Fax (202) 638-4004
Childrenofprisoners@cwla.org,
www.childrenofprisoners.org

Girl Scouts Beyond Bars
4806 Seton Pl.
Baltimore, MD 21215
(410) 358-9711; Fax (410) 358-9918
www.gscm.org

Legal Action Center
225 Varick St.
New York, NY 10014
(212) 243-1313; Fax: (212) 675-0286
lacinfol@lac.org
www.lac.org

Legal Services for Prisoners with Children
1540 Market St., Ste 490
San Francisco, CA 94102
(415) 255-7036
info@prisonerswithchildren.org

Narcotics Anonymous
World Service Office
P.O. Box 9999
Van Nuys, CA 91409
www.na.org

National Center for Lesbian Rights
870 Market St. #750
San Francisco, CA 94102
Hotline (415) 392-6257
www.nclrights.org

National Coalition Against Domestic Violence
P.O. Box 18749
Denver, CO 80218
www.ncadv.org

Network for Battered Lesbians/La Red
P.O. Box 6011
Boston, MA 02114
(617) 423-SAFE
www.thenetworklared.org

National Indian Child Welfare Association
5100 SW Macadam Ave, Ste 300
Portland, OR 97230
http://www.nicwa.org

Rape, Abuse and Incest National Network
1-800-656-HOPE
www.rainn.org

Survivors of Incest Anonymous
World Service Office
P.O. Box 190
Benson, MD 21018
www.siawso.org

VOICES in Action, Inc.
Network of Abuse Survivors
P.O. Box 148309
Chicago, IL 60614
www.voices-action.org

Women for Sobriety
P.O. Box 618
Quakertown, PA 18951
www.womenforsobriety.org

Books for Children of Incarcerated Mothers

Bergen, Suzanne, and Kathleen Hodgkins. 1997. *My Mom Went to Jail.* The Rainbow Project, Inc., 831 E. Washington Avenue, Madison, Wisconsin 53703. **(ages 6-10)**

Black, Frank M. 1990. *It's Not Your Fault, Sweetheart.* Inside-OUT Publishing. Available through Active Parenting Publishers, Inc., 1955 Vaughn Rd. NW, Suite 108, Kennesaw, Georgia 30144.

Black, Frank M. 1999. *There Are Some Real Special Kids in Our Class.* Inside-OUT Publishing. Available through Active Parenting Publishers, Inc., 1955 Vaughn Rd. NW, Suite 108, Kennesaw, Georgia 30144.

Black, Frank M. 1999. *A Visit with Mommy.* 1999 Inside-OUT Publishing. Available through Active Parenting Publishers, Inc., 1955 Vaughn Rd. NW, Suite 108, Kennesaw, Georgia 30144.

Brisson, Pat. 2004. *Mama Loves Me from Away.* Illustrated by Laurie A. Caple. Boyds Mills Press, 815 Church Street, Honesdale, PA 18431. **(ages 5–10)**

Butterworth, Oliver. 1993. *A Visit to the Big House.* Illustrated by Susan Avishai. Boston: Houghton Mifflin Company. **(ages 7–10)**

Gesme, Carole 1993. *Help for Kids: Understanding Your Feelings about Having a Parent in Prison or Jail.* Pine Tree Press, 4036 Kerry Court, Minnetonka, Minnesota 55345. **(ages 6 and older)**

Rosenkrantz, Louise, ed. 1984. *I Know How You Feel Because This Happened to Me: A Handbook for Kids with a Parent in Prison.* Center for Children with Incarcerated Parents. Berkeley, California 94708: Prison MATCH. **(ages 7–8)**

Wittbold, Maureen. 1998. *Let's Talk about When Your Parent Is in Jail.* New York: Rosen Publishing Group. **(ages 5–12)**

Woodson, Jacqueline. 2002. *Our Gracie Aunt.* Illustrated by Jon J. Muth. New York: Jump at the Sun. **(ages 4–8)**

About the Authors

Diane E. Stawar, M.A., LMHC, LCC, is a counselor at Brandon's House Counseling Center in New Albany, Indiana, and manages Jeffbook in Jeffersonville, Indiana for LifeSpring Inc. Jeffbook is a working retail used bookstore that also serves as a transitional work program. It provides training and work experience for people with serious and persistent mental illness. Ms. Stawar has served as a counselor, psychological examiner, mediator, and coordinator of a children's program for more than thirty years in community mental health settings.

She served on a Human Rights Advocacy Committee in Florida investigating human rights complaints against publicly funded facilities. She also served as a guardian-at-litem, investigating and speaking in court for children in dependency cases, especially those involving sexual abuse. She also has done divorce mediations, setting up primary residence and visitation agreements.

She has worked extensively with children and families as well as adult sexual abuse victims. Ms. Stawar is a Licensed Mental Health Counselor in the state of Indiana and a Licensed Professional Clinical Counselor in the State of Kentucky. She and her husband, Terry, have one daughter, three sons, and three grandchildren.

Terry L. Stawar, Ed.D., LMHC, LSP, is the chief executive officer of Lifespring, Inc., a community mental health center serving Southern Indiana. Dr. Stawar has more than thirty years of experience in community mental health. He is licensed as a school psychologist and mental health counselor and is a certified psychiatric rehabilitation practitioner. Dr. Stawar is a member of the American Correctional Association, the American Psychological Association, the U.S. Psychiatric Rehabilitation Association, and is a Fellow of the American College of Forensic Examiners, a diplomate in school psychology of the American Board of Psychological Specialties, and serves on the Commission on Forensic Education.

As a psychotherapist, psychological examiner, clinical supervisor, and administrator, he has worked extensively with parents and children and has managed several programs providing psychological services in correctional settings. Dr. Stawar also has conducted several research studies, writes a weekly newspaper column, and has published popular and professional articles on a wide range of topics, from antisocial personality disorder to the psychological assessment of adolescents.